Speech Steps ®

Reproducible Drills for Artic and Language

Written by Andrea Herson, M.A., CCC-SLP, Joanne Sabin, M.A., CCC-SLP and Ashley Drennan
Edited by Thomas Webber
Illustrated by Steve Barr, Kari Bolt, Chuck Hart, Bill Golliher, Jack Vaughan,
Tawnia Lechner, Tony Mitchell, and Ryan Bradburn

Post Office Box 24997, Greenville, South Carolina 29616
Call Toll Free 1-800-277-8737 • Fax Toll Free 1-800-978-7379
Online! www.superduperinc.com
E-Mail: custserv@superduperinc.com

ISBN 1-58650-244-1

Dedication

This book is dedicated to all the children and parents who have

so eagerly enjoyed "these steps" towards good speech and

language. It is from their enthusiasm and successes over 35

years that we have been inspired to now share this program.

-Andrea Herson, M.A., CCC-SLP has 25 years of clinical experience in the Maryland school system working with the deaf and hard-of-hearing, severe speech and language disabled students, and more recently, with pre-school children through private practice. In addition, "Andee" served as President of the Speech and Hearing Discussion Group of the Metropolitan Area for more than 17 years.

-Joanne Sabin, M.A., CCC-SLP served as Director of a children's center, founded and directed a Speech Pathology Department in a hospital setting, and has clinical experience in a variety of settings including private practice.

Introduction

The **Speech Steps**® Program is an easy, extremely beneficial program, for young children in the initial stages of therapy. The program includes exercises for basic imitation of vowels to word production by using pictures with targeted sounds in various positions of simple words (CV, CVC, CVCV, etc.). Using these **Steps** in short, frequent sessions will promote optimal learning. As the child's vocabulary increases, continue to lead the child to good speech development by copying the pictures and using them with other fun games, or start the child on his/her personalized **Step** Program using the open-ended seasonal **Steps** on pages 160-170. Therapists, parents, and teachers will enjoy using these **Steps** for children with articulation delays, apraxia, and autism.

The program consists of:

1. **Vowel production**: Start each child at this basic level to set the format for other sounds. Since they are easier to imitate, begin each program with long vowels.
2. **Simple word production (CV, CVC, CVCV)**: Gradually progress from consonant-vowel production to consonant-vowel-consonant and then to consonant-vowel-consonant-vowel production in simple words.
3. **Blends and more complex structures (CCVC, CVCCVC, CVCVCV, etc.)**: Add more words to growing vocabulary using words with more complex structures.

HINTS:

- Use imitation for all steps. If a word is too difficult for the child, continue to stimulate it, and accept whatever the child says at the time.
- Write the symbol for the sound at the top of the page. Touch the symbol and say its sound. This promotes phonemic awareness allowing children to learn sound-symbol associations.
- Encourage children to climb the steps to successful production of sounds and words with rewards such as chips, tokens, cards, or other reinforcements.
- Cut small squares of cardboard and write different symbols (b, m, f, etc.) on them. Pick one to use as a marker as you climb up the steps. The child keeps the marker as a reward when he/she gets to the top.
- Turn the faces on the vowel page into clowns by drawing a hat on the head. Outline the mouths in red to emphasize the mouth shape.
- As the child is able to say a word, copy and paste it on an index card to begin a word file box. Use these cards for games such as memory, tic-tac-toe, guessing games, etc. Children love to see their words grow.
- Nothing takes the place of the enthusiasm and excitement of the speech helper. Remember to make it fun!

Table of Contents

#BK-303 Speech Steps® • ©2002 Super Duper® Publications • 1-800-277-8737 • Online! www.superduperinc.com

Table of Contents

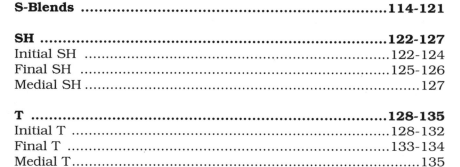

Parent/Helper Letter

Date:_____

Dear Parent/Homework Helper: _____

      Your child is currently using **Speech Steps**® **Reproducible Drills** to work on _____ in class. You can help your child's progress by completing the attached activity sheet.

☐ Please sign the worksheet in the designated spot and return it to me by _____.

☐ Please complete this sheet at home. You do not need to return it to me. Keep it at home in a file for extra practice sessions.

      Have fun helping your child develop his/her speech and language skills!

      Thank you,

_____   _____
        Name   Parent/Helper's Signature

#BK-303 Speech Steps® • ©2002 Super Duper® Publications • 1-800-277-8737 • Online! www.superduperinc.com

Vowel Practice

Instructions: Have the student practice saying each sound as he/she goes up the steps. The speech helper says each sound and exaggerates the mouth movement. Then, have the student repeat the sound. Practice in front of a mirror when possible. It is suggested to say each sound one time, (ex: a, e, i, o, u,) then two times, (ex: a-a, e-e, i-i, o-o, u-u,) and then three times (ex: a-a-a, e-e-e, i-i-i, o-o-o, u-u-u). Also, vary the sounds (ex: a-o, e-i, etc.).

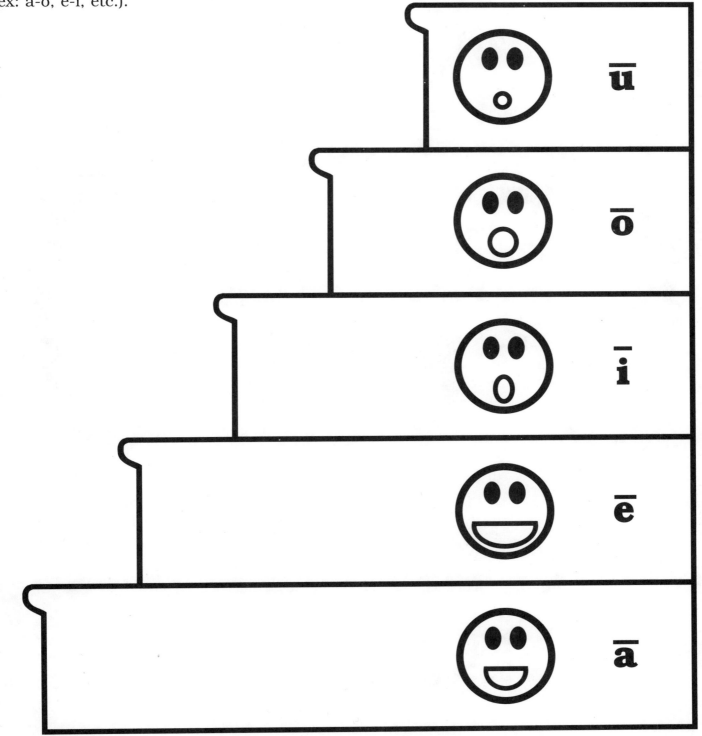

Homework Partner   Date   Name   **Long Vowels**

Vowel Practice

Instructions: Cut out the clown and the mouth. Have the student place his/her mouth in the opening and practice vowel sounds to help increase awareness of tongue movement. Practice in front of a mirror when possible.

| Homework Partner | Date | Name |

#BK-303 Speech Steps® • ©2002 Super Duper® Publications • 1-800-277-8737 • Online! www.superduperinc.com

Vowel Practice

Vowel Practice

Instructions: Have the student color the clown hats and outline the mouths in red to emphasize the mouth shapes. Then, have the student show or imitate each clown's mouth in the mirror. Cut out and mix up the sounds for extra practice.

Speech Steps

Instructions: Have the student practice saying each sound/word as he/she goes up the steps. The speech helper will read/say each sound/word. Then, have the student repeat the sounds/words. Practice in front of a mirror when possible.

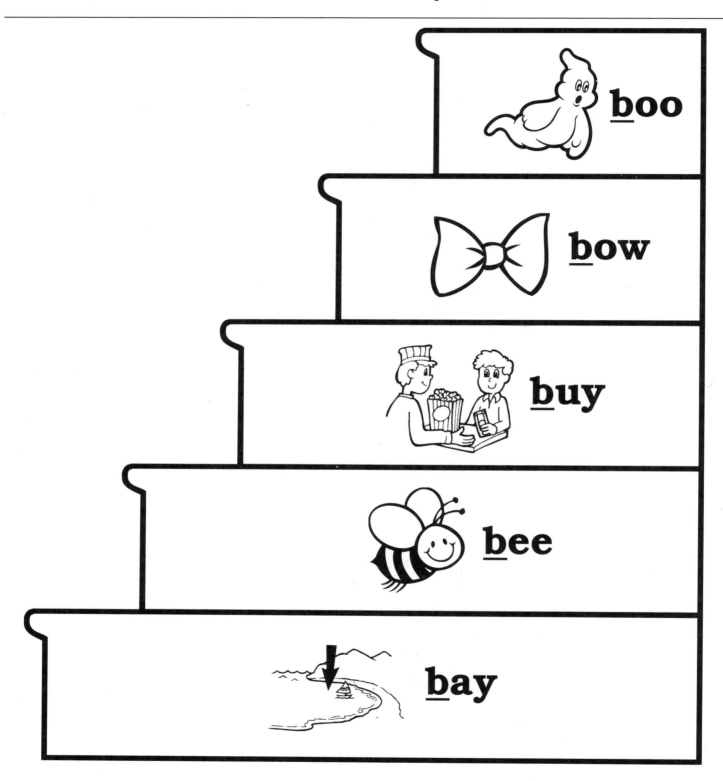

Initial B Long Vowels

Speech Steps

Instructions: Have the student practice saying each sound/word as he/she goes up the steps. The speech helper will read/say each sound/word. Then, have the student repeat the sounds/words. Practice in front of a mirror when possible.

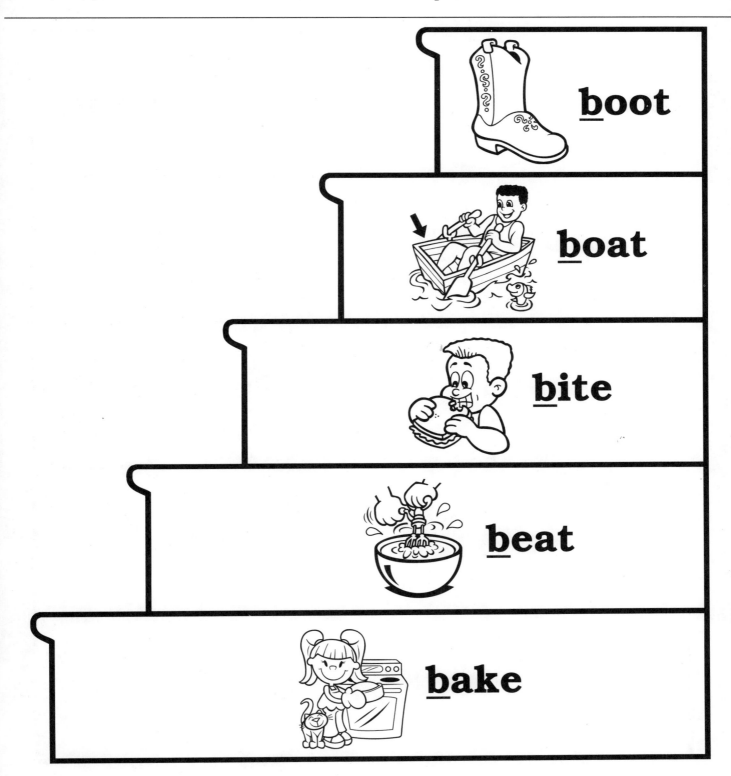

boot

boat

bite

beat

bake

Homework Partner   Date   Name

**Initial B
Long Vowels**

Speech Steps

Instructions: Have the student practice saying each sound/word as he/she goes up the steps. The speech helper will read/say each sound/word. Then, have the student repeat the sounds/words. Practice in front of a mirror when possible.

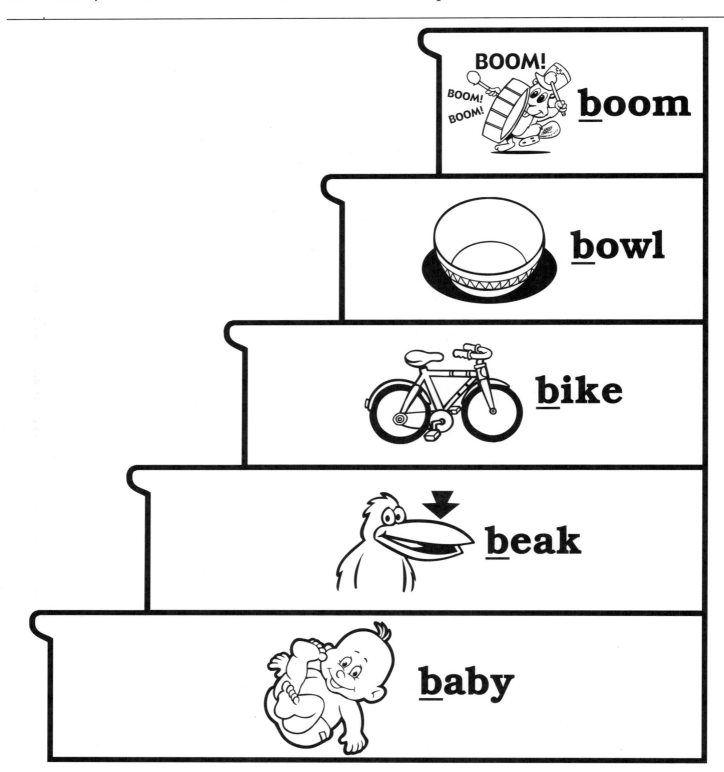

#BK-303 Speech Steps® • ©2002 Super Duper® Publications • 1-800-277-8737 • Online! www.superduperinc.com

Speech Steps

Instructions: Have the student practice saying each sound/word as he/she goes up the steps. The speech helper will read/say each sound/word. Then, have the student repeat the sounds/words. Practice in front of a mirror when possible.

bug

box

big

bed

back

Homework Partner   Date   Name   **Initial B Short Vowels**

Speech Steps

Instructions: Have the student practice saying each sound/word as he/she goes up the steps. The speech helper will read/say each sound/word. Then, have the student repeat the sounds/words. Practice in front of a mirror when possible.

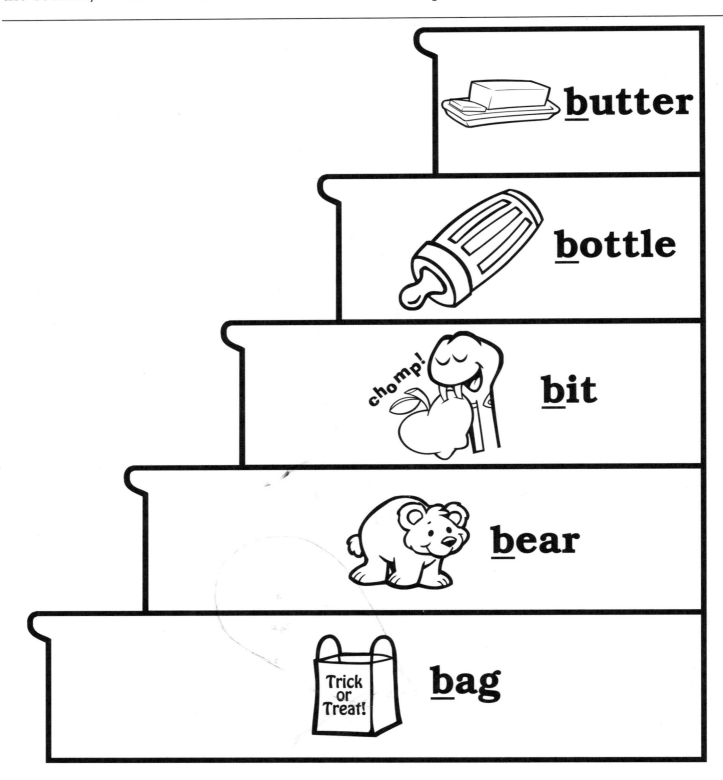

__butter__

__bottle__

chomp! __bit__

__bear__

Trick or Treat! __bag__

Speech Steps

Instructions: Have the student practice saying each sound/word as he/she goes up the steps. The speech helper will read/say each sound/word. Then, have the student repeat the sounds/words. Practice in front of a mirror when possible.

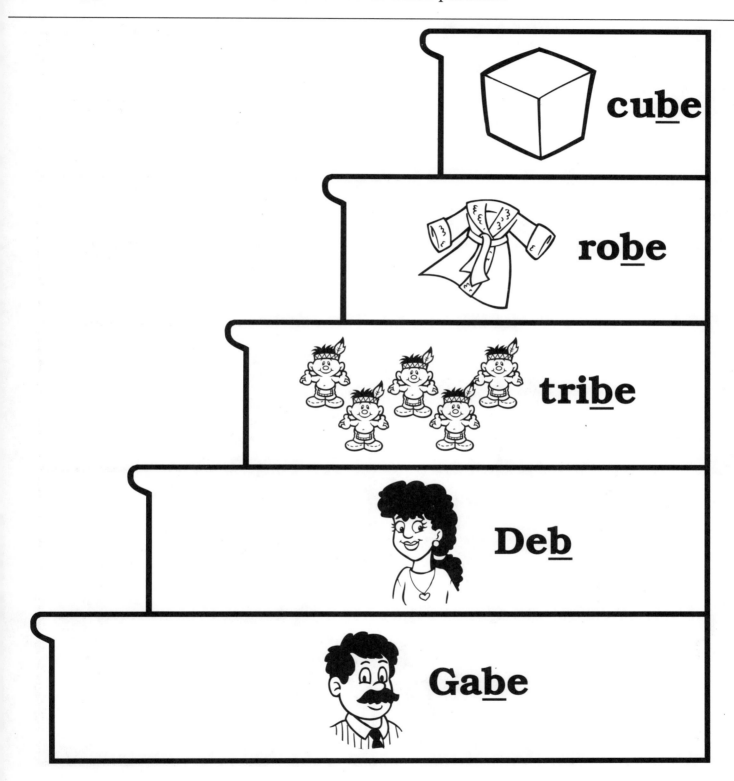

cube

robe

tribe

Deb

Gabe

Speech Steps

Instructions: Have the student practice saying each sound/word as he/she goes up the steps. The speech helper will read/say each sound/word. Then, have the student repeat the sounds/words. Practice in front of a mirror when possible.

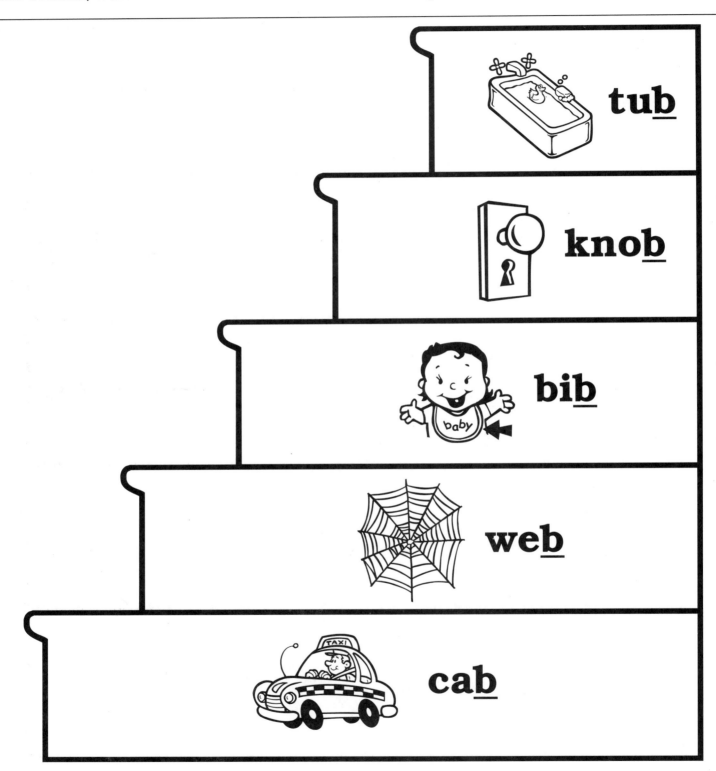

tu**b**

kno**b**

bi**b**

we**b**

ca**b**

**Final B
Short Vowels**

Speech Steps

Instructions: Have the student practice saying each sound/word as he/she goes up the steps. The speech helper will read/say each sound/word. Then, have the student repeat the sounds/words. Practice in front of a mirror when possible.

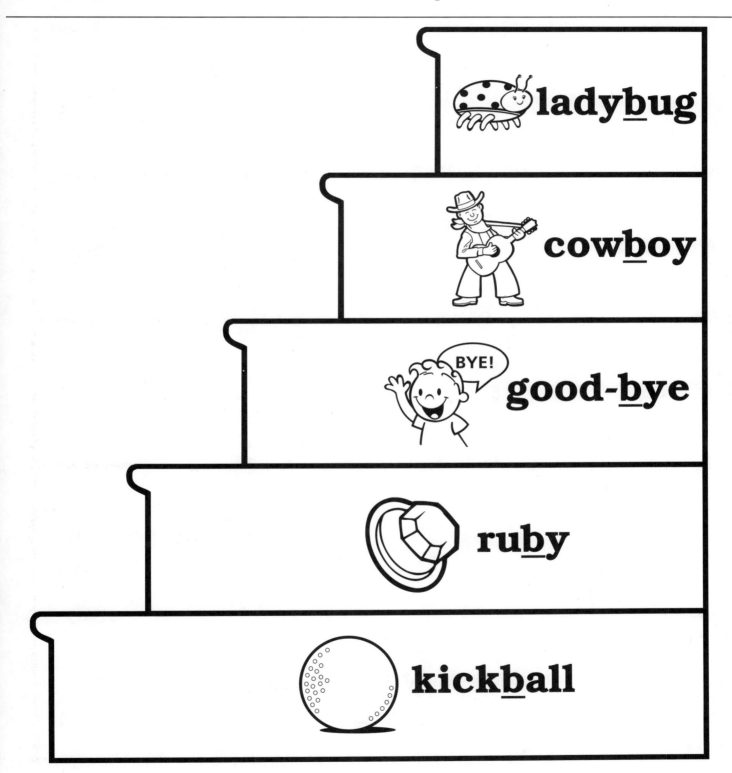

ladybug

cowboy

good-bye

ruby

kickball

Homework Partner   Date   Name

**Medial B
Combo Vowels**

Speech Steps

Instructions: Have the student practice saying each sound/word as he/she goes up the steps. The speech helper will read/say each sound/word. Then, have the student repeat the sounds/words. Practice in front of a mirror when possible.

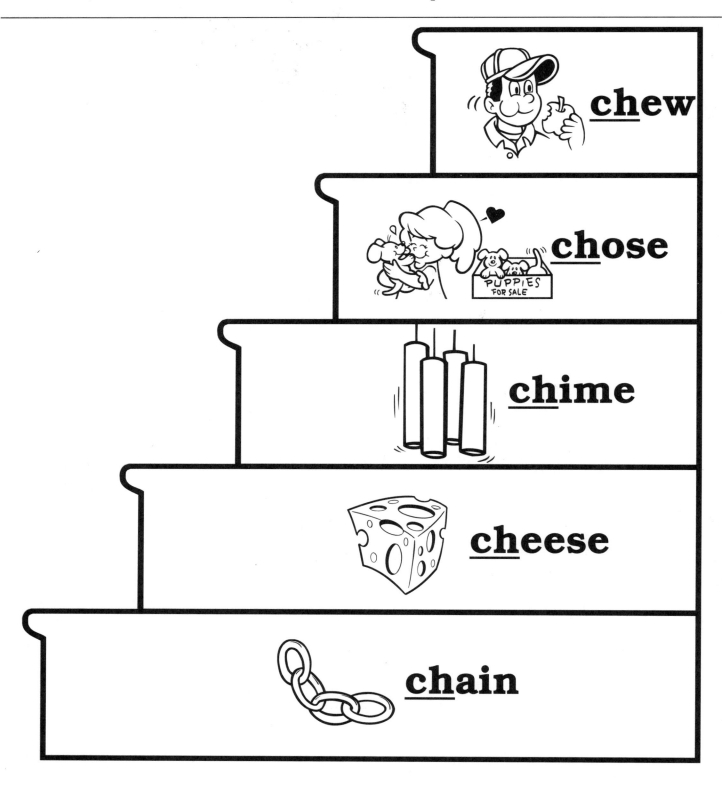

chew

chose

PUPPIES FOR SALE

chime

cheese

chain

Speech Steps

Instructions: Have the student practice saying each sound/word as he/she goes up the steps. The speech helper will read/say each sound/word. Then, have the student repeat the sounds/words. Practice in front of a mirror when possible.

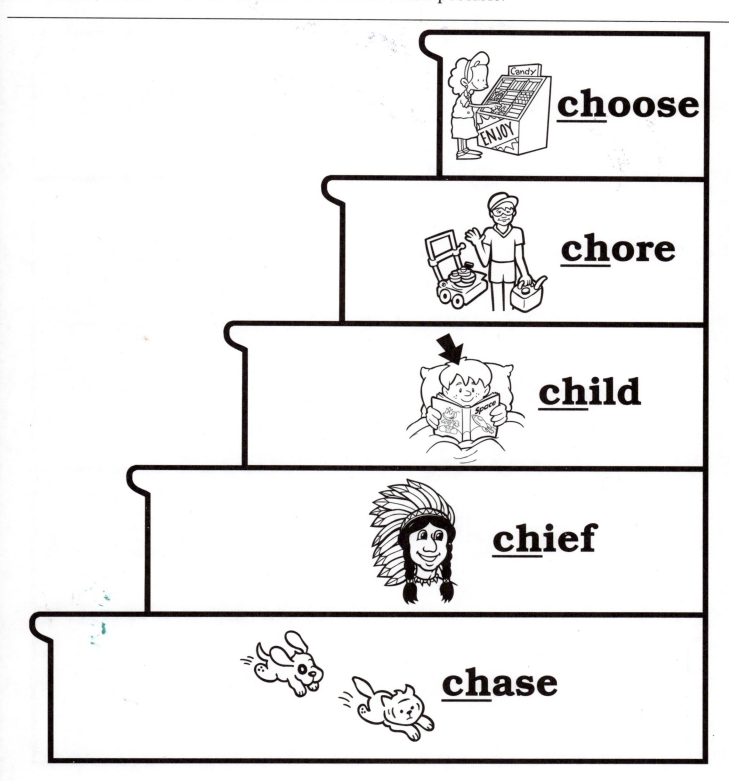

choose

chore

child

chief

chase

#BK-303 Speech Steps® • ©2002 Super Duper® Publications • 1-800-277-8737 • Online! www.superduperinc.com

13

Speech Steps

Instructions: Have the student practice saying each sound/word as he/she goes up the steps. The speech helper will read/say each sound/word. Then, have the student repeat the sounds/words. Practice in front of a mirror when possible.

Chuck

chop

chin

check

chair

Homework Partner   Date   Name

**Initial CH
Short Vowels**

#BK-303 Speech Steps® • ©2002 Super Duper® Publications • 1-800-277-8737 • Online! www.superduperinc.com

Speech Steps

Instructions: Have the student practice saying each sound/word as he/she goes up the steps. The speech helper will read/say each sound/word. Then, have the student repeat the sounds/words. Practice in front of a mirror when possible.

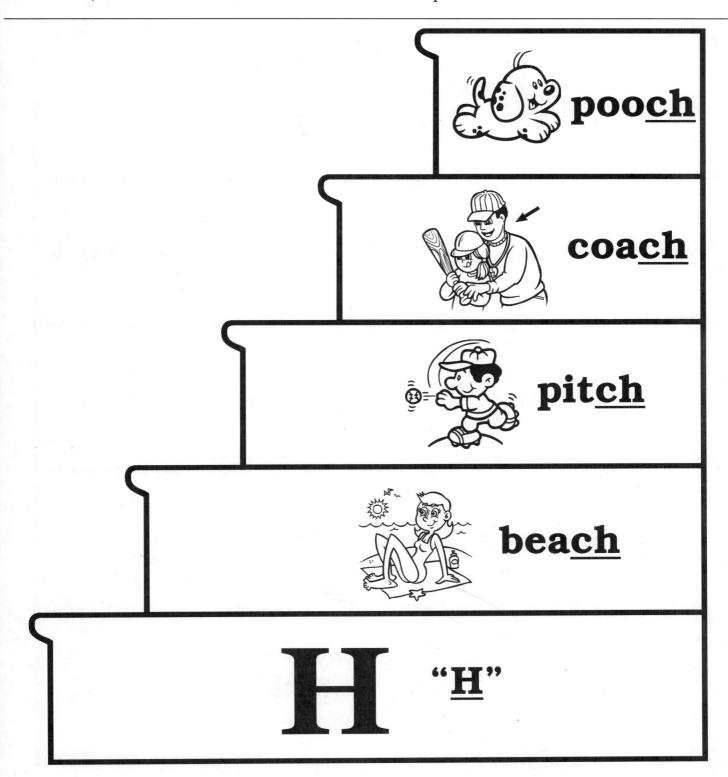

pooch

coach

pitch

beach

H   "**H**"

Speech Steps

Instructions: Have the student practice saying each sound/word as he/she goes up the steps. The speech helper will read/say each sound/word. Then, have the student repeat the sounds/words. Practice in front of a mirror when possible.

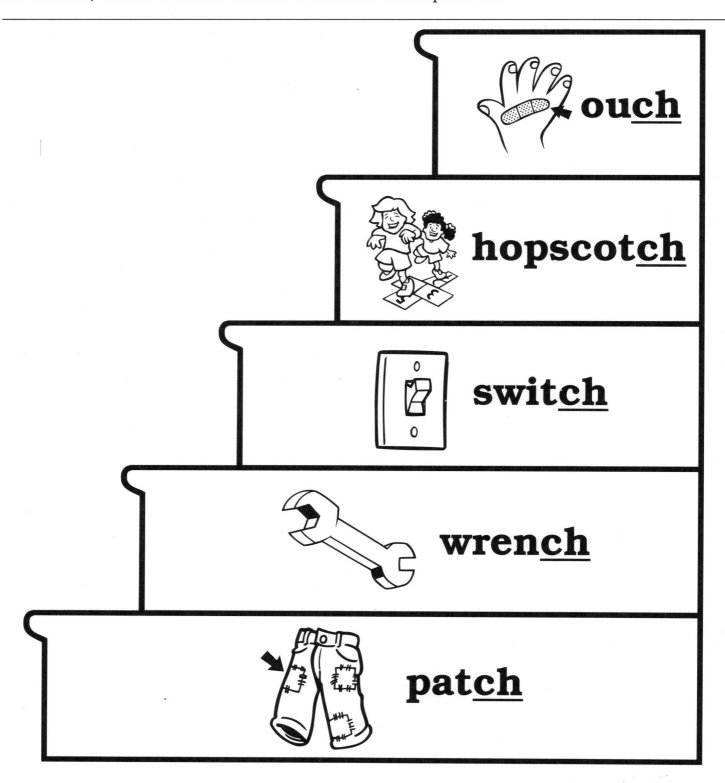

ou<u>ch</u>

hopscot<u>ch</u>

swit<u>ch</u>

wren<u>ch</u>

pat<u>ch</u>

Homework Partner   Date   Name

Final CH Combo Vowels

#BK-303 Speech Steps® • ©2002 Super Duper® Publications • 1-800-277-8737 • Online! www.superduperinc.com

Speech Steps

Instructions: Have the student practice saying each sound/word as he/she goes up the steps. The speech helper will read/say each sound/word. Then, have the student repeat the sounds/words. Practice in front of a mirror when possible.

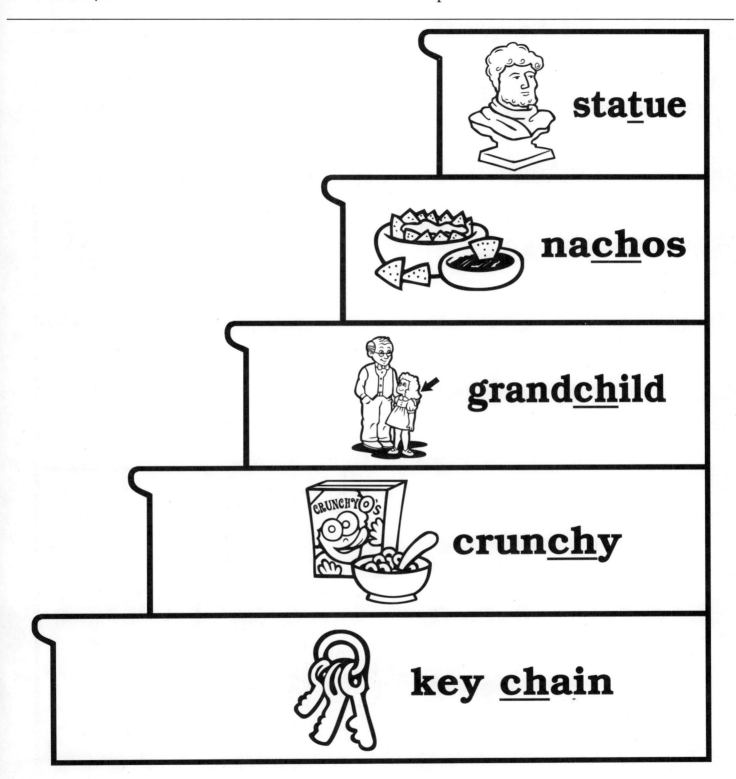

statue

nachos

grandchild

crunchy

key chain

Homework Partner   Date   Name   **Medial CH Combo Vowels**

#BK-303 Speech Steps® • ©2002 Super Duper® Publications • 1-800-277-8737 • Online! www.superduperinc.com   17

Speech Steps

Instructions: Have the student practice saying each sound/word as he/she goes up the steps. The speech helper will read/say each sound/word. Then, have the student repeat the sounds/words. Practice in front of a mirror when possible.

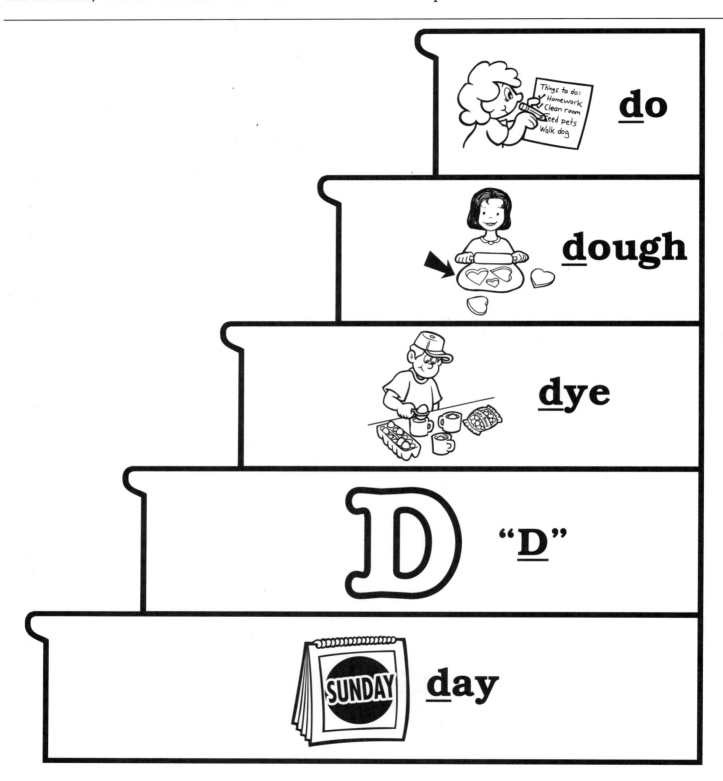

do

dough

dye

"D"

day

Homework Partner   Date   Name

#BK-303 Speech Steps® • ©2002 Super Duper® Publications • 1-800-277-8737 • Online! www.superduperinc.com

Speech Steps

Instructions: Have the student practice saying each sound/word as he/she goes up the steps. The speech helper will read/say each sound/word. Then, have the student repeat the sounds/words. Practice in front of a mirror when possible.

dude

dome

dime

deep

date

Homework Partner   Date   Name

Speech Steps

Instructions: Have the student practice saying each sound/word as he/she goes up the steps. The speech helper will read/say each sound/word. Then, have the student repeat the sounds/words. Practice in front of a mirror when possible.

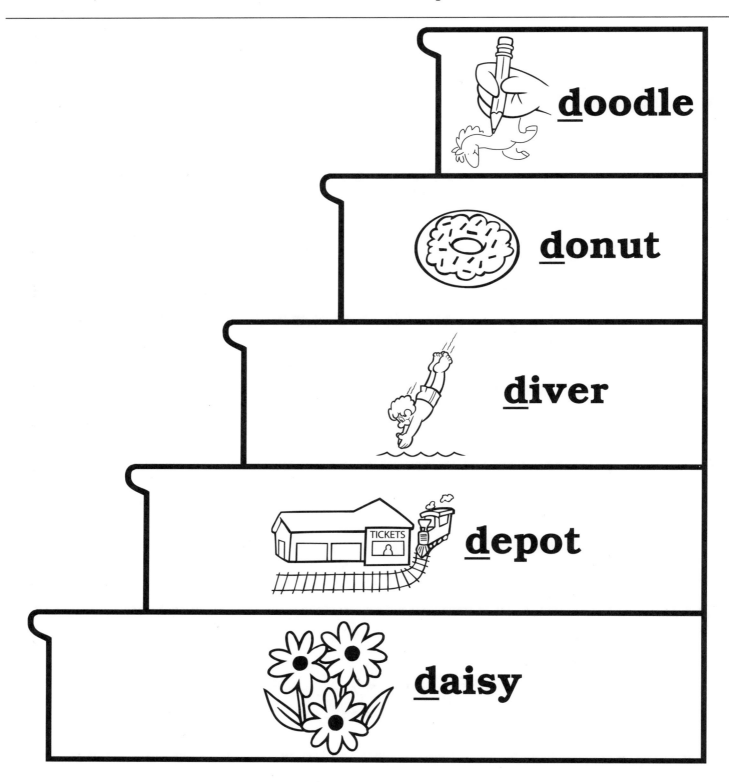

doodle

donut

diver

depot

daisy

Speech Steps

Instructions: Have the student practice saying each sound/word as he/she goes up the steps. The speech helper will read/say each sound/word. Then, have the student repeat the sounds/words. Practice in front of a mirror when possible.

Homework Partner   Date   Name

Initial D
Short Vowels

Speech Steps

Instructions: Have the student practice saying each sound/word as he/she goes up the steps. The speech helper will read/say each sound/word. Then, have the student repeat the sounds/words. Practice in front of a mirror when possible.

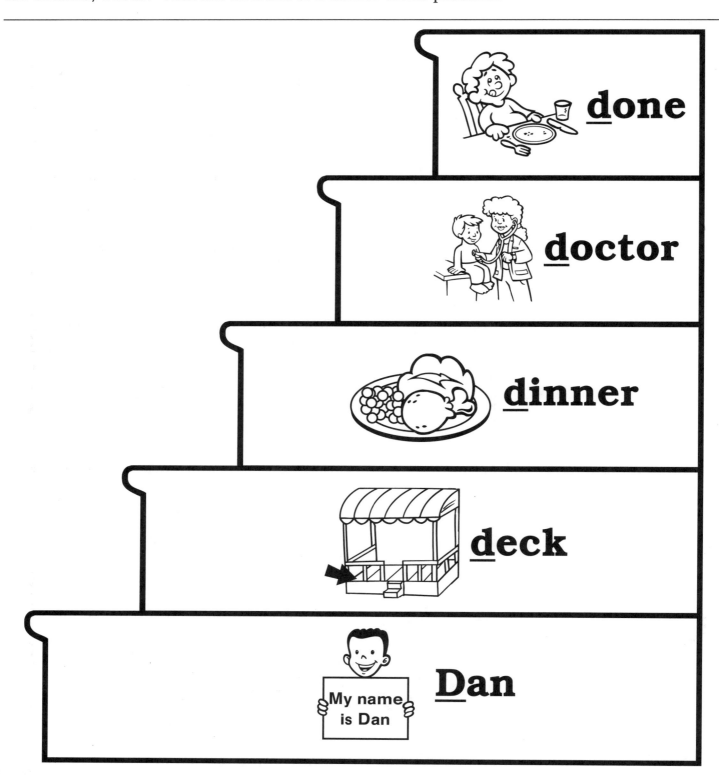

done

doctor

dinner

deck

Dan

My name is Dan

Initial D Short Vowels

#BK-303 Speech Steps® • ©2002 Super Duper® Publications • 1-800-277-8737 • Online! www.superduperinc.com

Speech Steps

Instructions: Have the student practice saying each sound/word as he/she goes up the steps. The speech helper will read/say each sound/word. Then, have the student repeat the sounds/words. Practice in front of a mirror when possible.

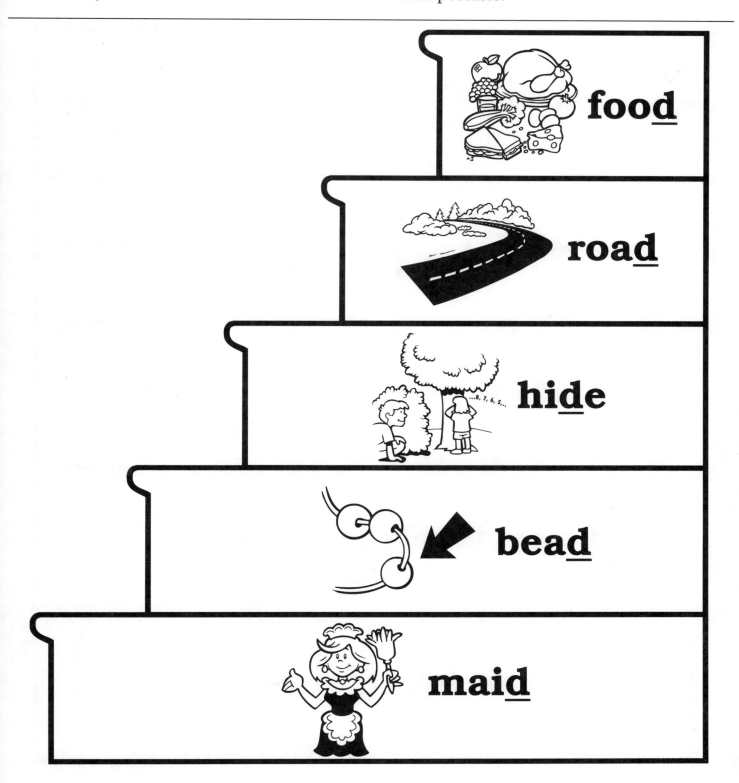

food

road

hide

bead

maid

Homework Partner   Date   Name

Final D Long Vowels

Speech Steps

Instructions: Have the student practice saying each sound/word as he/she goes up the steps. The speech helper will read/say each sound/word. Then, have the student repeat the sounds/words. Practice in front of a mirror when possible.

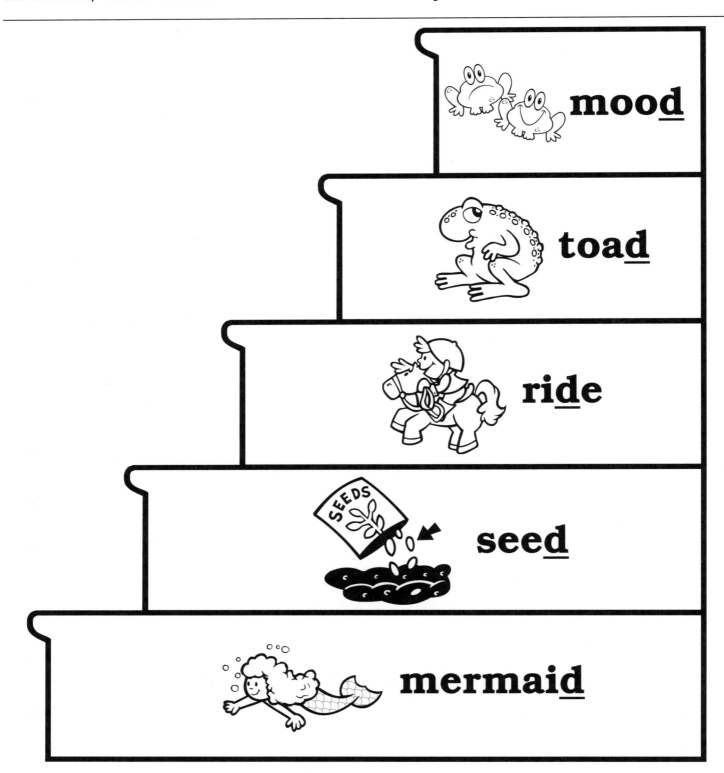

mood

toad

ride

seed

mermaid

Speech Steps

Instructions: Have the student practice saying each sound/word as he/she goes up the steps. The speech helper will read/say each sound/word. Then, have the student repeat the sounds/words. Practice in front of a mirror when possible.

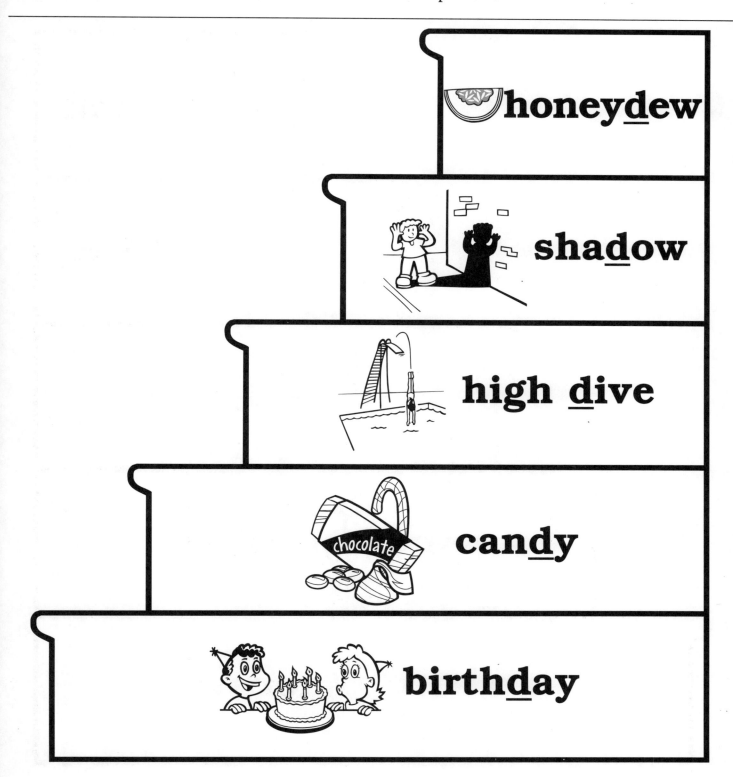

honeydew

shadow

high dive

candy

birthday

Homework Partner   Date   Name

Medial D Combo Vowels

Speech Steps

Instructions: Have the student practice saying each sound/word as he/she goes up the steps. The speech helper will read/say each sound/word. Then, have the student repeat the sounds/words. Practice in front of a mirror when possible.

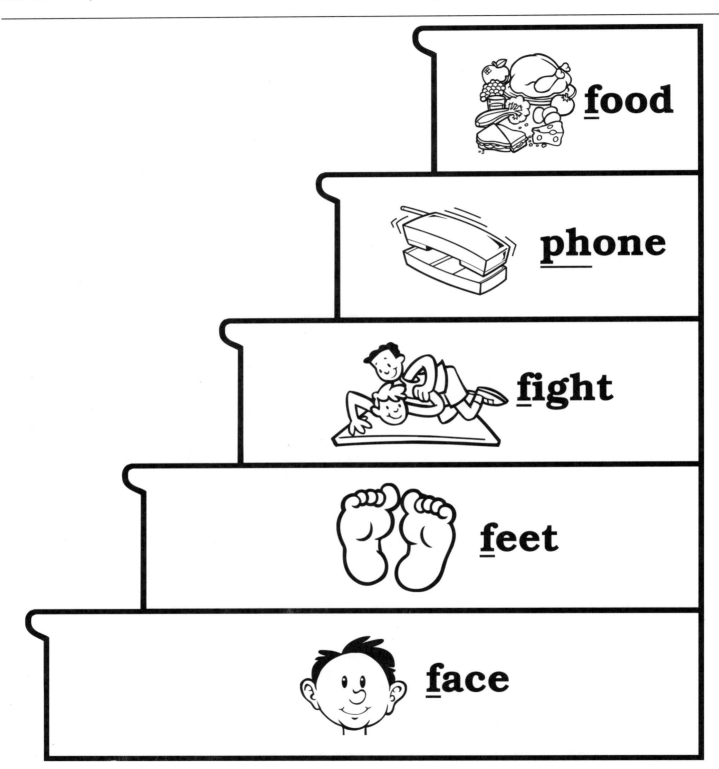

food

phone

fight

feet

face

Homework Partner   Date   Name

**Initial F
Long Vowels**

#BK-303 Speech Steps® • ©2002 Super Duper® Publications • 1-800-277-8737 • Online! www.superduperinc.com

Speech Steps

Instructions: Have the student practice saying each sound/word as he/she goes up the steps. The speech helper will read/say each sound/word. Then, have the student repeat the sounds/words. Practice in front of a mirror when possible.

Homework Partner   Date   Name

Speech Steps

Instructions: Have the student practice saying each sound/word as he/she goes up the steps. The speech helper will read/say each sound/word. Then, have the student repeat the sounds/words. Practice in front of a mirror when possible.

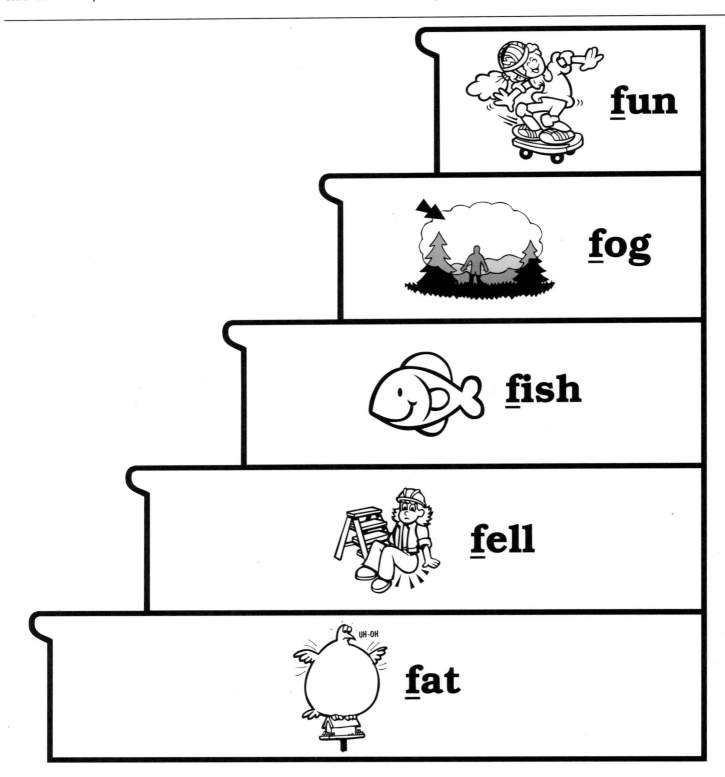

<u>f</u>un

<u>f</u>og

<u>f</u>ish

<u>f</u>ell

<u>f</u>at

_____ _____ _____

Homework Partner   Date   Name

**Initial F
Short Vowels**

#BK-303 Speech Steps® • ©2002 Super Duper® Publications • 1-800-277-8737 • Online! www.superduperinc.com

Speech Steps

Instructions: Have the student practice saying each sound/word as he/she goes up the steps. The speech helper will read/say each sound/word. Then, have the student repeat the sounds/words. Practice in front of a mirror when possible.

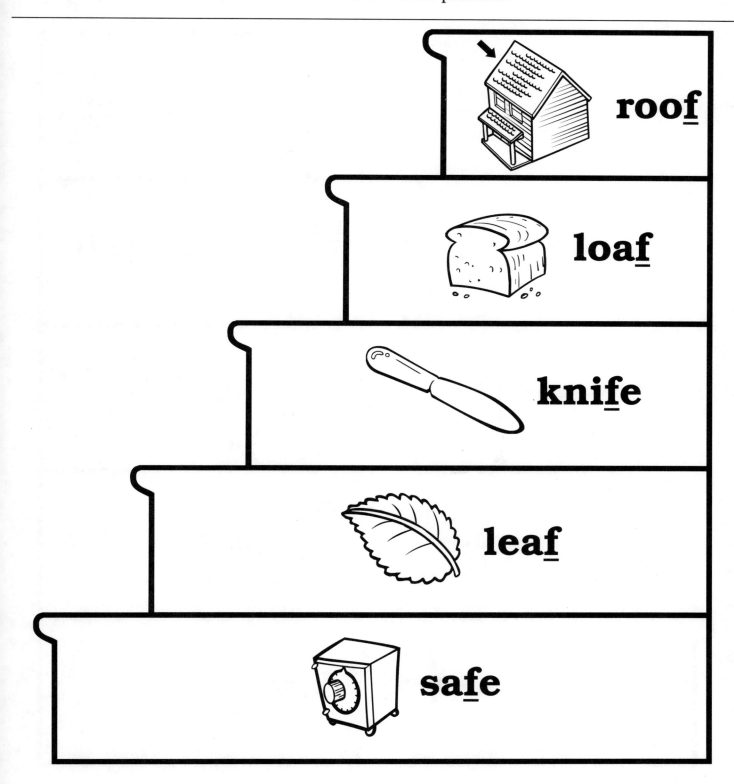

roof

loaf

knife

leaf

safe

Homework Partner   Date   Name

Final F Long Vowels

Speech Steps

Instructions: Have the student practice saying each sound/word as he/she goes up the steps. The speech helper will read/say each sound/word. Then, have the student repeat the sounds/words. Practice in front of a mirror when possible.

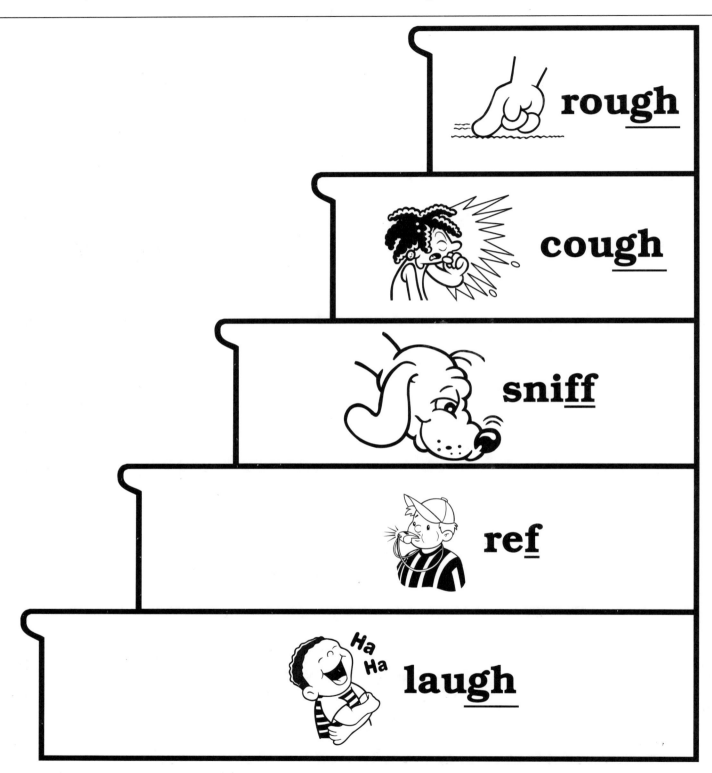

rou<u>gh</u>

cou<u>gh</u>

sni<u>ff</u>

re<u>f</u>

lau<u>gh</u>

Homework Partner   Date   Name

Speech Steps

Instructions: Have the student practice saying each sound/word as he/she goes up the steps. The speech helper will read/say each sound/word. Then, have the student repeat the sounds/words. Practice in front of a mirror when possible.

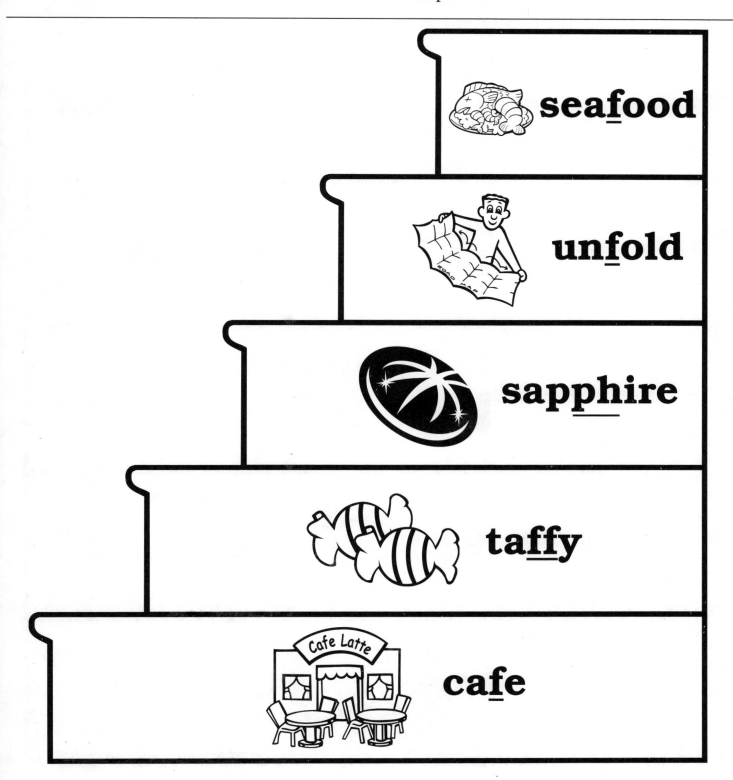

seafood

unfold

sapphire

taffy

Cafe Latte

cafe

Speech Steps

Instructions: Have the student practice saying each sound/word as he/she goes up the steps. The speech helper will read/say each sound/word. Then, have the student repeat the sounds/words. Practice in front of a mirror when possible.

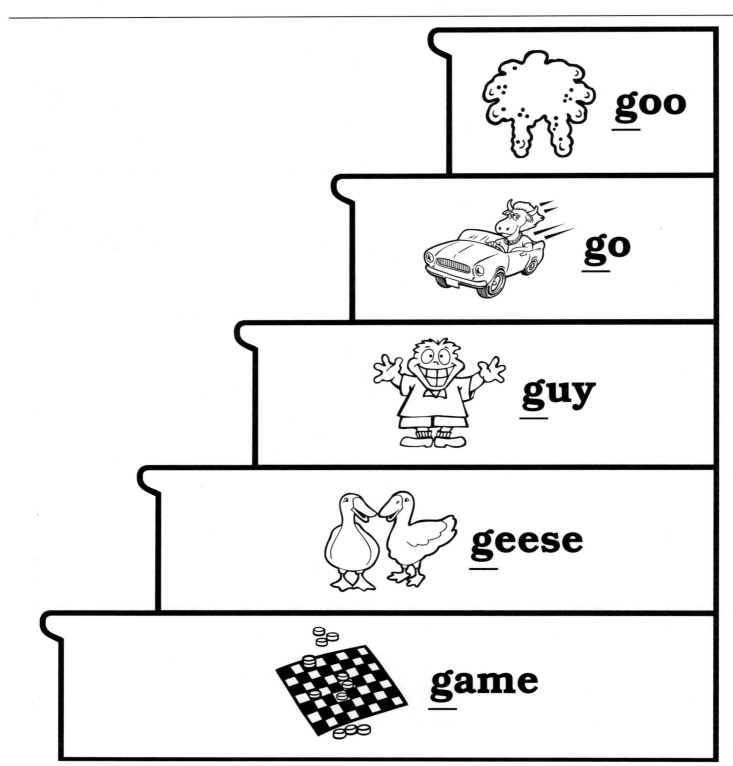

goo

go

guy

geese

game

Homework Partner   Date   Name

Initial G
Long Vowels

Speech Steps

Instructions: Have the student practice saying each sound/word as he/she goes up the steps. The speech helper will read/say each sound/word. Then, have the student repeat the sounds/words. Practice in front of a mirror when possible.

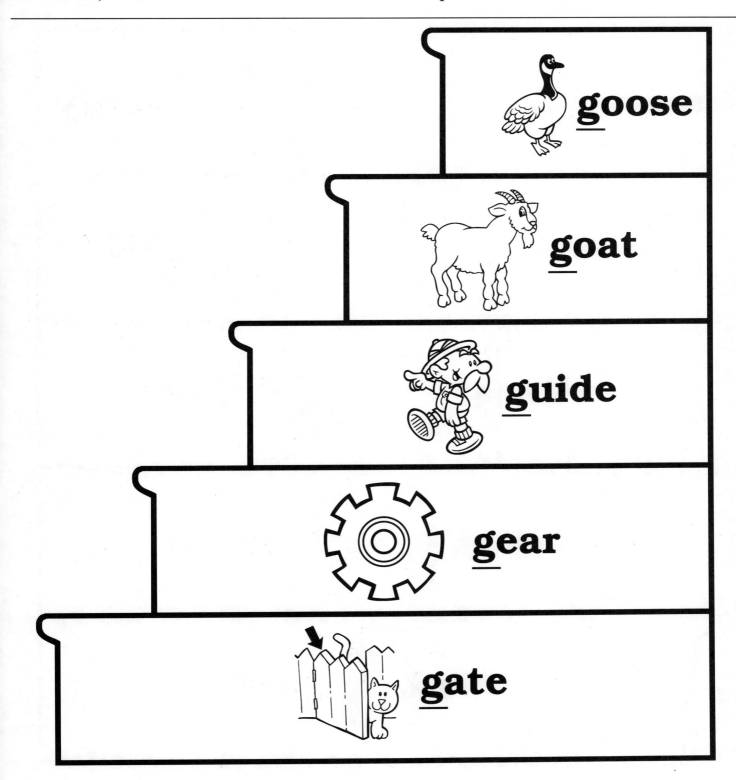

goose

goat

guide

gear

gate

Homework Partner   Date   Name

Initial G Combo Vowels

Speech Steps

Instructions: Have the student practice saying each sound/word as he/she goes up the steps. The speech helper will read/say each sound/word. Then, have the student repeat the sounds/words. Practice in front of a mirror when possible.

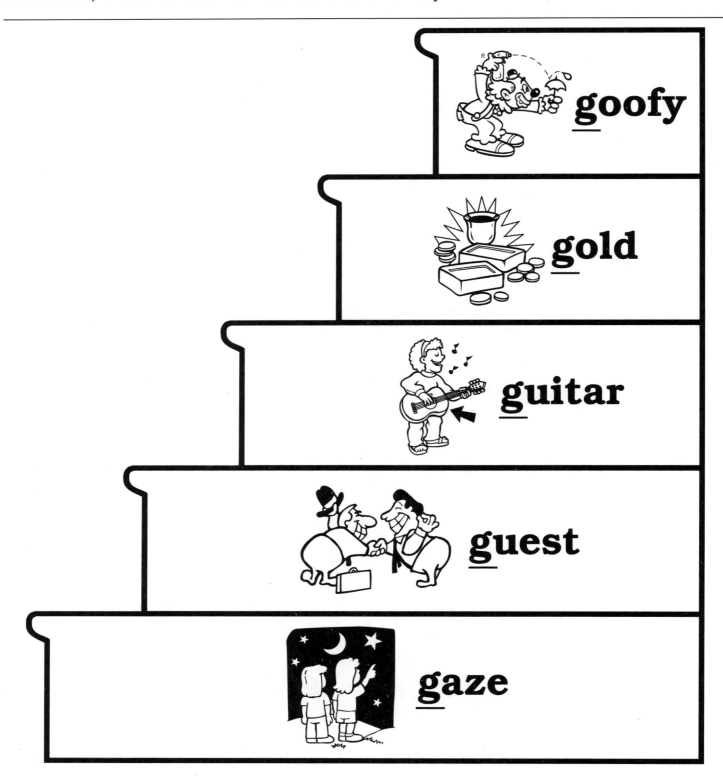

goofy

gold

guitar

guest

gaze

#BK-303 Speech Steps® • ©2002 Super Duper® Publications • 1-800-277-8737 • Online! www.superduperinc.com

Speech Steps

Instructions: Have the student practice saying each sound/word as he/she goes up the steps. The speech helper will read/say each sound/word. Then, have the student repeat the sounds/words. Practice in front of a mirror when possible.

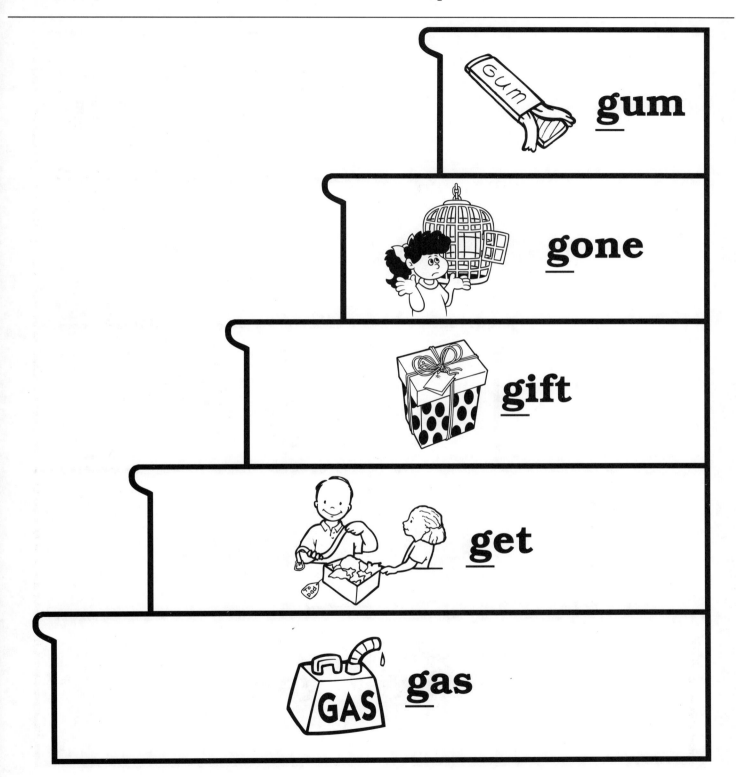

gum

gone

gift

get

gas

Homework Partner   Date   Name

Speech Steps

Instructions: Have the student practice saying each sound/word as he/she goes up the steps. The speech helper will read/say each sound/word. Then, have the student repeat the sounds/words. Practice in front of a mirror when possible.

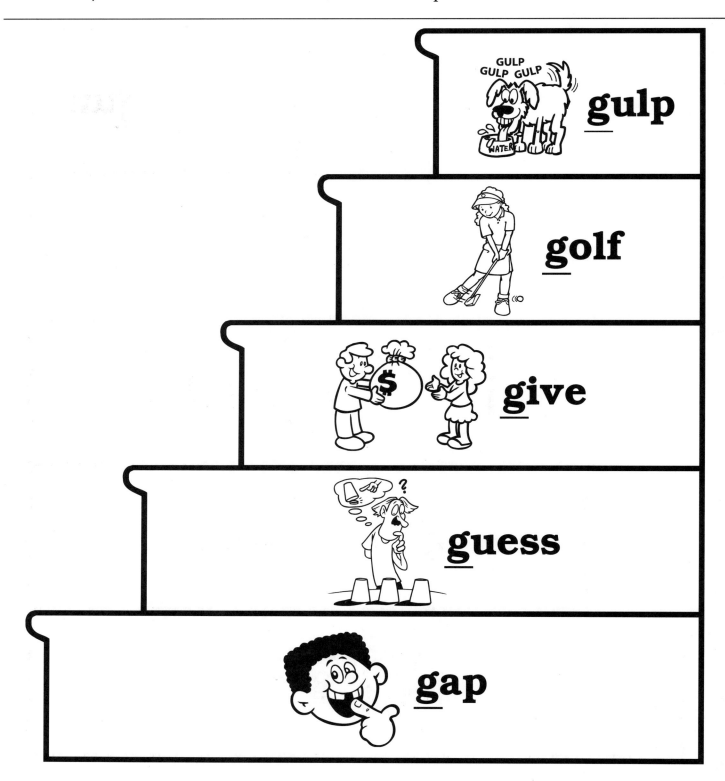

_____ _____ _____

Homework Partner   Date   Name

#BK-303 Speech Steps® • ©2002 Super Duper® Publications • 1-800-277-8737 • Online! www.superduperinc.com

Speech Steps

Instructions: Have the student practice saying each sound/word as he/she goes up the steps. The speech helper will read/say each sound/word. Then, have the student repeat the sounds/words. Practice in front of a mirror when possible.

Homework Partner   Date   Name

Speech Steps

Instructions: Have the student practice saying each sound/word as he/she goes up the steps. The speech helper will read/say each sound/word. Then, have the student repeat the sounds/words. Practice in front of a mirror when possible.

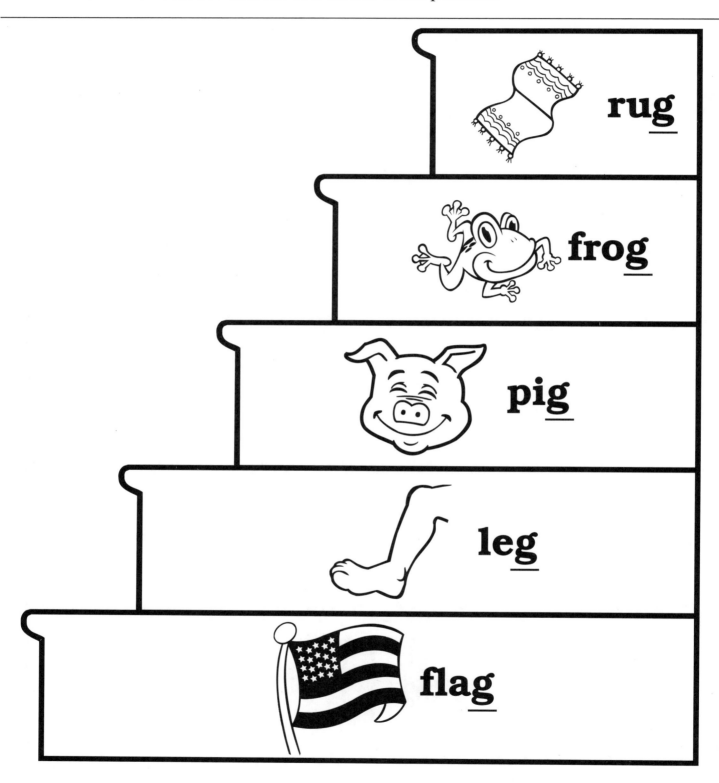

rug

frog

pig

leg

flag

**Final G
Short Vowels**

#BK-303 Speech Steps® • ©2002 Super Duper® Publications • 1-800-277-8737 • Online! www.superduperinc.com

Speech Steps

Instructions: Have the student practice saying each sound/word as he/she goes up the steps. The speech helper will read/say each sound/word. Then, have the student repeat the sounds/words. Practice in front of a mirror when possible.

dragon

cargo

disguise

buggy

sugar

Homework Partner   Date   Name

Medial G Combo Vowels

Speech Steps

Instructions: Have the student practice saying each sound/word as he/she goes up the steps. The speech helper will read/say each sound/word. Then, have the student repeat the sounds/words. Practice in front of a mirror when possible.

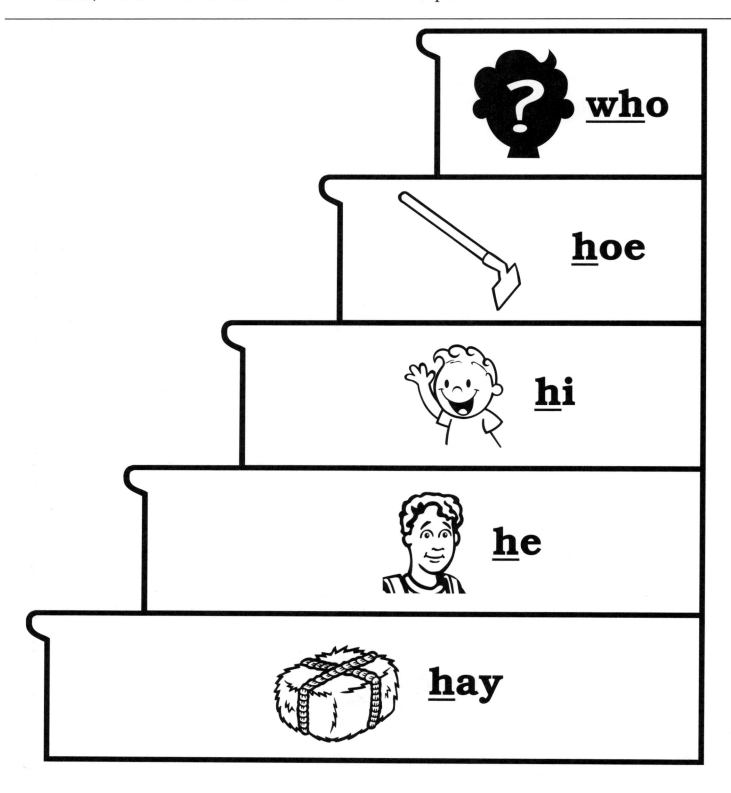

#BK-303 Speech Steps® • ©2002 Super Duper® Publications • 1-800-277-8737 • Online! www.superduperinc.com

Speech Steps

Instructions: Have the student practice saying each sound/word as he/she goes up the steps. The speech helper will read/say each sound/word. Then, have the student repeat the sounds/words. Practice in front of a mirror when possible.

| Homework Partner | Date | Name | **Initial H Long Vowels** |

Speech Steps

Instructions: Have the student practice saying each sound/word as he/she goes up the steps. The speech helper will read/say each sound/word. Then, have the student repeat the sounds/words. Practice in front of a mirror when possible.

_**h**ula

_**h**ome

_**h**ide

_**h**eat

_**h**air

#BK-303 Speech Steps® • ©2002 Super Duper® Publications • 1-800-277-8737 • Online! www.superduperinc.com

Speech Steps

Instructions: Have the student practice saying each sound/word as he/she goes up the steps. The speech helper will read/say each sound/word. Then, have the student repeat the sounds/words. Practice in front of a mirror when possible.

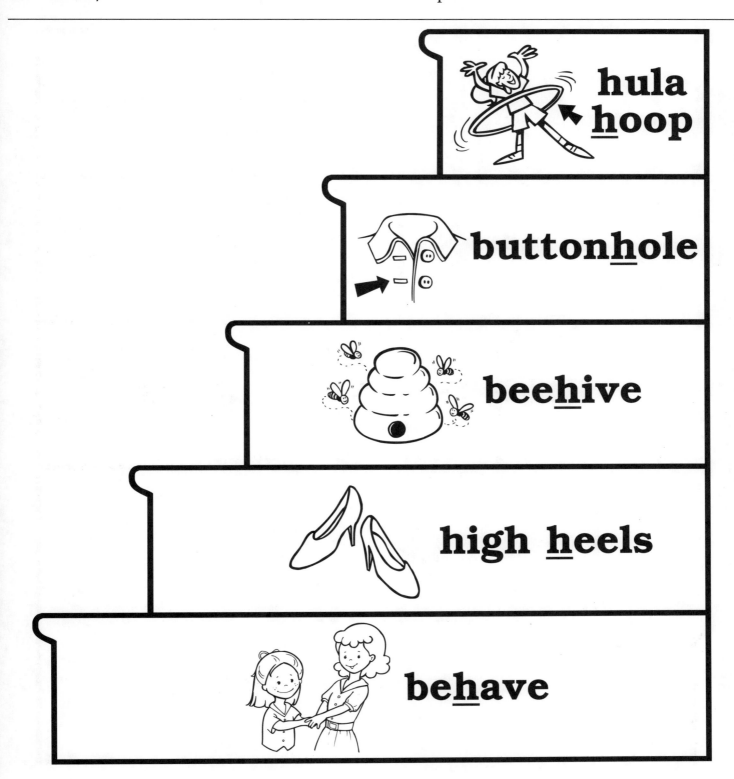

hula
hoop

buttonhole

beehive

high heels

behave

Speech Steps

Instructions: Have the student practice saying each sound/word as he/she goes up the steps. The speech helper will read/say each sound/word. Then, have the student repeat the sounds/words. Practice in front of a mirror when possible.

<u>J</u>une

<u>J</u>oan

<u>g</u>iant

<u>j</u>eep

<u>J</u>ames

Homework Partner   Date   Name

**Initial J
Long Vowels**

#BK-303 Speech Steps® • ©2002 Super Duper® Publications • 1-800-277-8737 • Online! www.superduperinc.com

Speech Steps

Instructions: Have the student practice saying each sound/word as he/she goes up the steps. The speech helper will read/say each sound/word. Then, have the student repeat the sounds/words. Practice in front of a mirror when possible.

#BK-303 Speech Steps® • ©2002 Super Duper® Publications • 1-800-277-8737 • Online! www.superduperinc.com

Speech Steps

Instructions: Have the student practice saying each sound/word as he/she goes up the steps. The speech helper will read/say each sound/word. Then, have the student repeat the sounds/words. Practice in front of a mirror when possible.

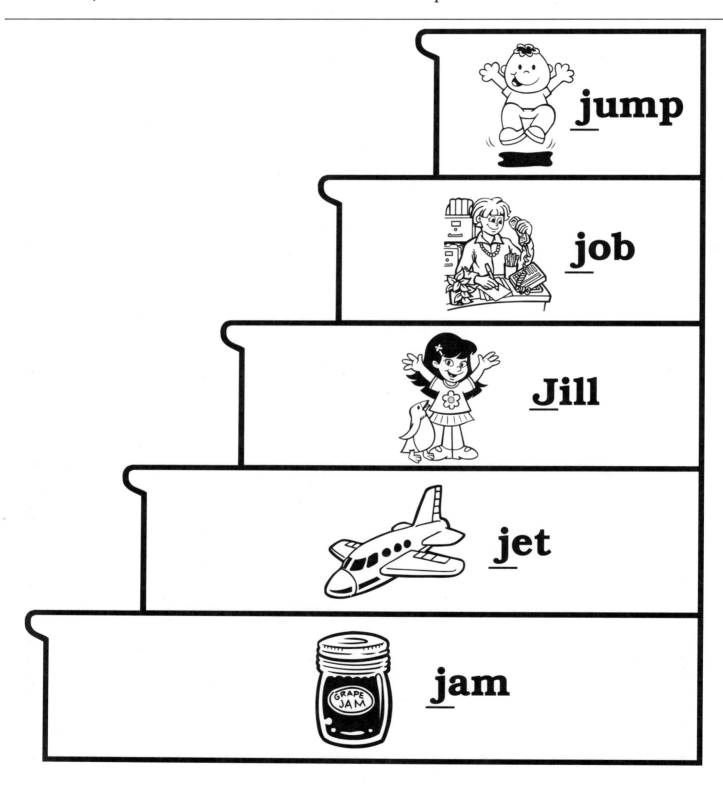

Homework Partner   Date   Name

46   #BK-303 Speech Steps® • ©2002 Super Duper® Publications • 1-800-277-8737 • Online! www.superduperinc.com

Speech Steps

Instructions: Have the student practice saying each sound/word as he/she goes up the steps. The speech helper will read/say each sound/word. Then, have the student repeat the sounds/words. Practice in front of a mirror when possible.

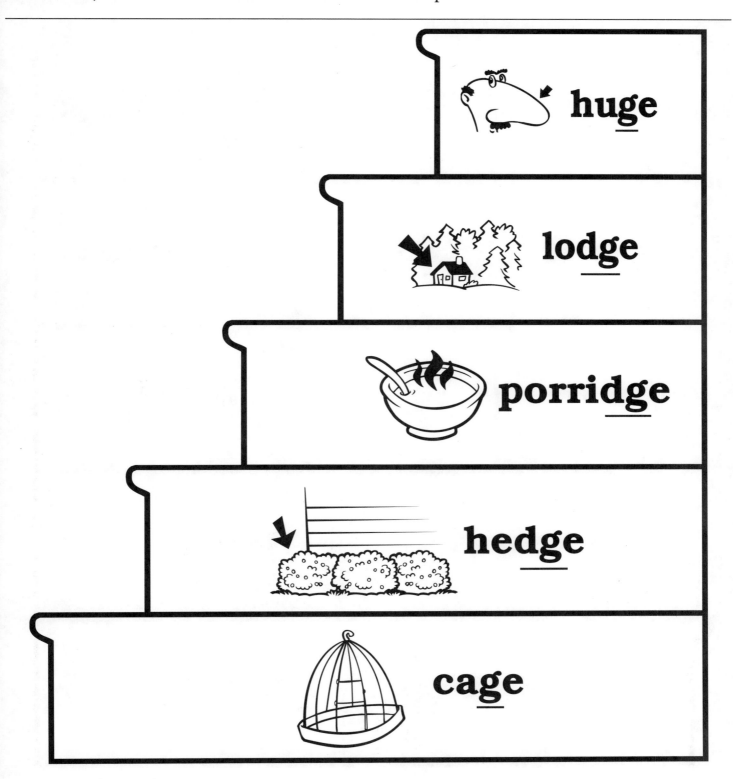

huge

lodge

porridge

hedge

cage

Homework Partner   Date   Name

Final J Combo Vowels

Speech Steps

Instructions: Have the student practice saying each sound/word as he/she goes up the steps. The speech helper will read/say each sound/word. Then, have the student repeat the sounds/words. Practice in front of a mirror when possible.

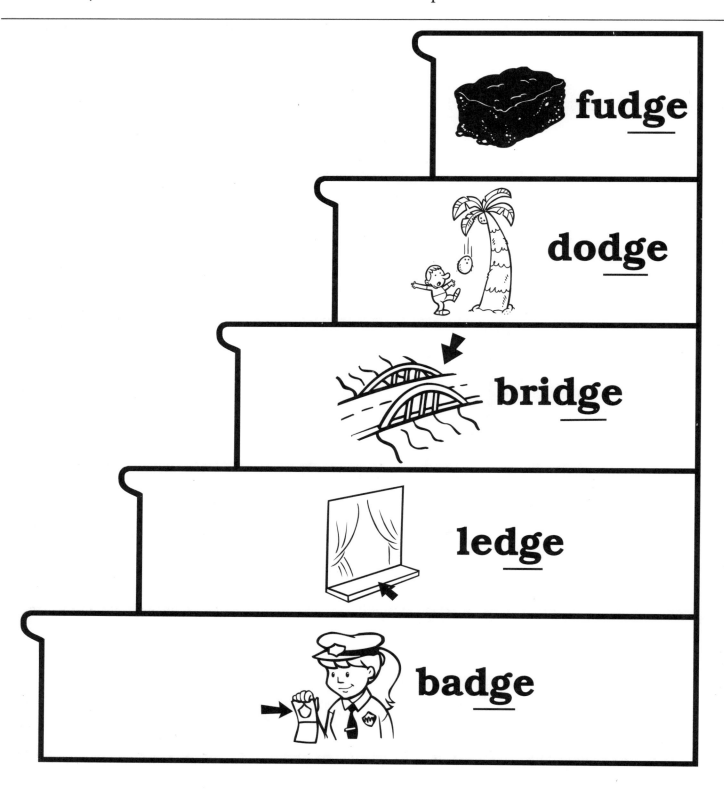

fudge

dodge

bridge

ledge

badge

#BK-303 Speech Steps® • ©2002 Super Duper® Publications • 1-800-277-8737 • Online! www.superduperinc.com

Speech Steps

Instructions: Have the student practice saying each sound/word as he/she goes up the steps. The speech helper will read/say each sound/word. Then, have the student repeat the sounds/words. Practice in front of a mirror when possible.

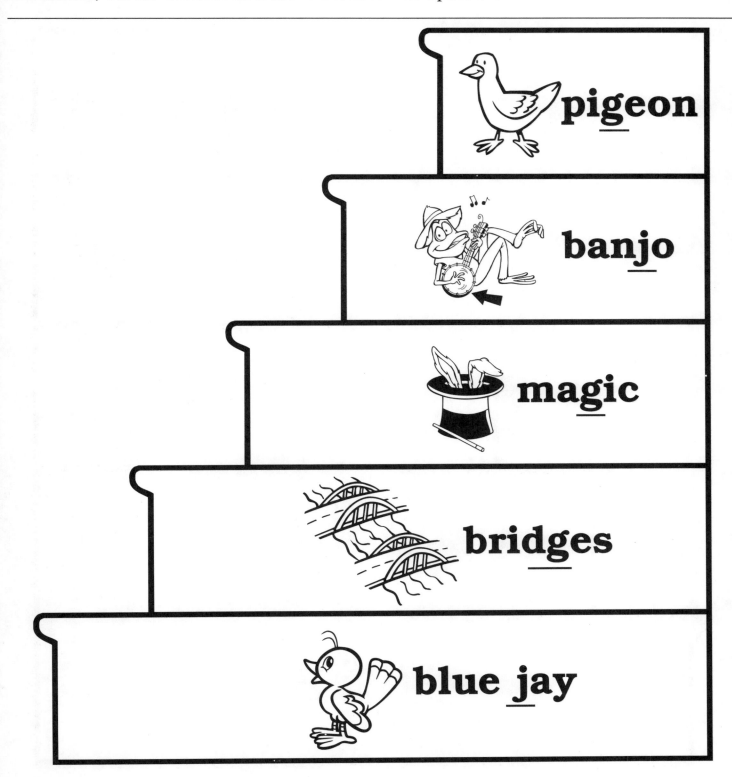

pigeon

banjo

magic

bridges

blue jay

Homework Partner   Date   Name

Medial J Combo Vowels

#BK-303 Speech Steps® • ©2002 Super Duper® Publications • 1-800-277-8737 • Online! www.superduperinc.com

Speech Steps

Instructions: Have the student practice saying each sound/word as he/she goes up the steps. The speech helper will read/say each sound/word. Then, have the student repeat the sounds/words. Practice in front of a mirror when possible.

__cool__

__coat__

__kite__

__key__

__Kate__

**Initial K
Long Vowels**

Speech Steps

Instructions: Have the student practice saying each sound/word as he/she goes up the steps. The speech helper will read/say each sound/word. Then, have the student repeat the sounds/words. Practice in front of a mirror when possible.

<u>c</u>oop

<u>c</u>one

<u>k</u>ind

<u>k</u>eep

<u>c</u>ape

Homework Partner   Date   Name

**Initial K
Long Vowels**

Speech Steps

Instructions: Have the student practice saying each sound/word as he/she goes up the steps. The speech helper will read/say each sound/word. Then, have the student repeat the sounds/words. Practice in front of a mirror when possible.

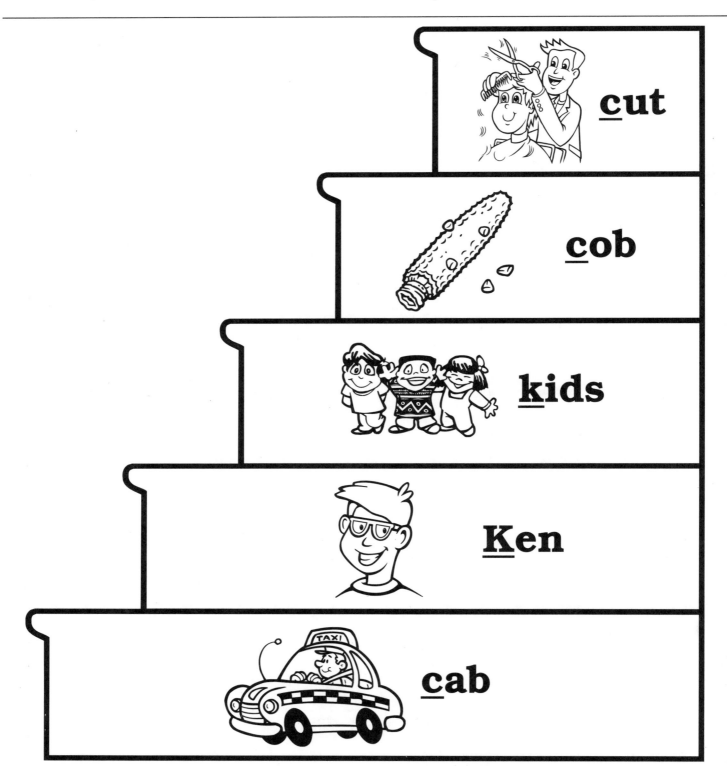

#BK-303 Speech Steps® • ©2002 Super Duper® Publications • 1-800-277-8737 • Online! www.superduperinc.com

Speech Steps

Instructions: Have the student practice saying each sound/word as he/she goes up the steps. The speech helper will read/say each sound/word. Then, have the student repeat the sounds/words. Practice in front of a mirror when possible.

cup

cop

kitten

ketchup

cat

Speech Steps

Instructions: Have the student practice saying each sound/word as he/she goes up the steps. The speech helper will read/say each sound/word. Then, have the student repeat the sounds/words. Practice in front of a mirror when possible.

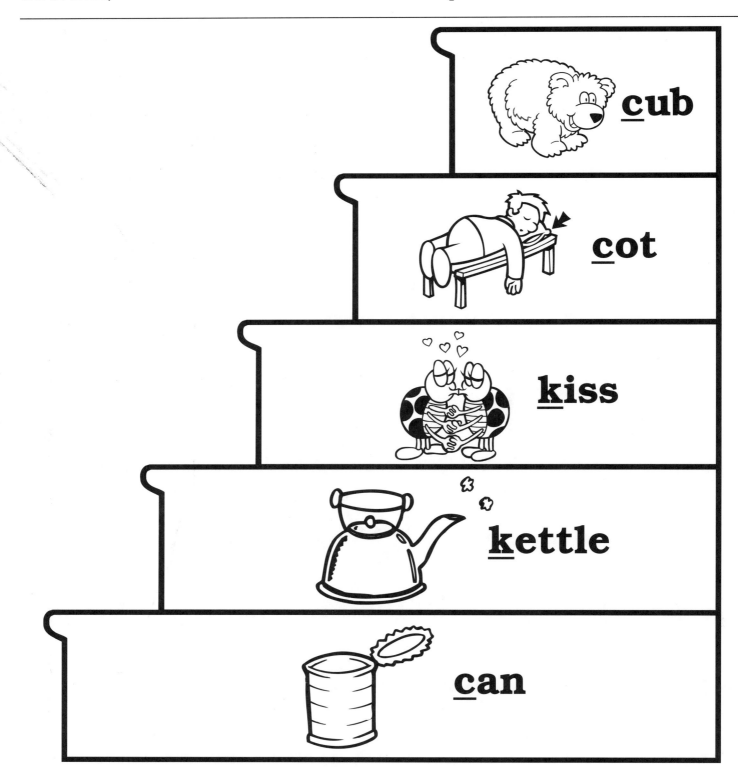

Initial K Short Vowels

#BK-303 Speech Steps® • ©2002 Super Duper® Publications • 1-800-277-8737 • Online! www.superduperinc.com

Speech Steps

Instructions: Have the student practice saying each sound/word as he/she goes up the steps. The speech helper will read/say each sound/word. Then, have the student repeat the sounds/words. Practice in front of a mirror when possible.

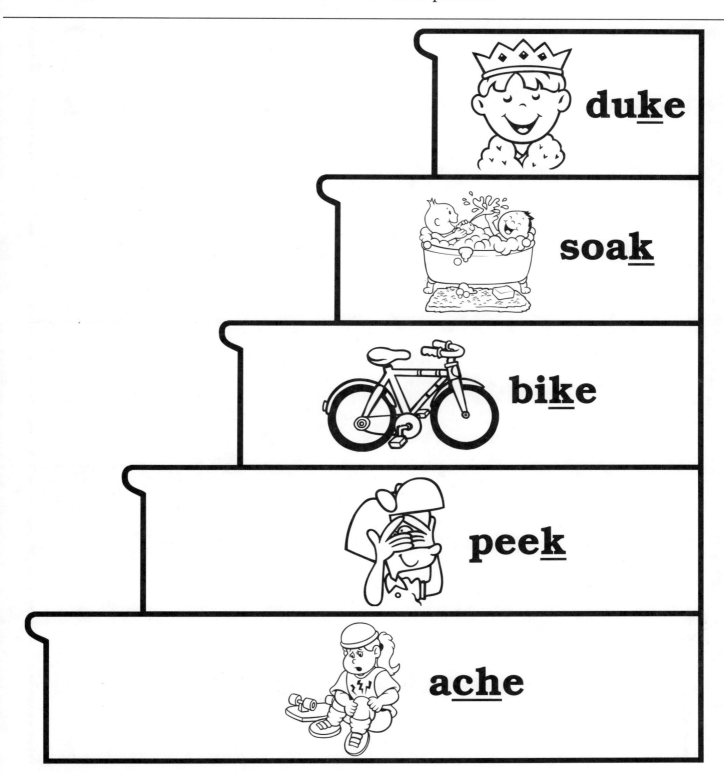

du<u>k</u>e

soa<u>k</u>

bi<u>k</u>e

pee<u>k</u>

a<u>ch</u>e

Homework Partner   Date   Name

**Final K
Long Vowels**

Speech Steps

Instructions: Have the student practice saying each sound/word as he/she goes up the steps. The speech helper will read/say each sound/word. Then, have the student repeat the sounds/words. Practice in front of a mirror when possible.

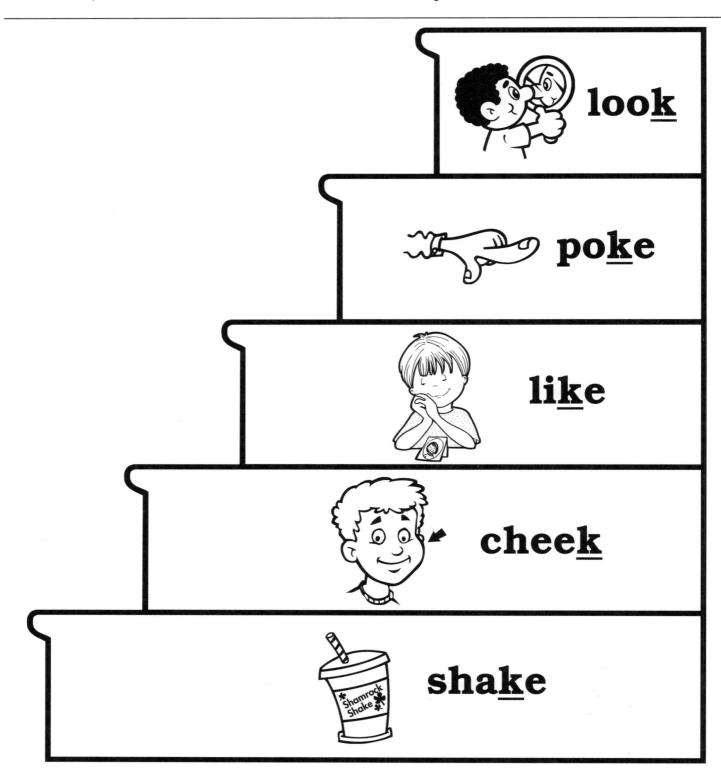

look

poke

like

cheek

shake

Homework Partner   Date   Name

Final K Combo Vowels

Speech Steps

Instructions: Have the student practice saying each sound/word as he/she goes up the steps. The speech helper will read/say each sound/word. Then, have the student repeat the sounds/words. Practice in front of a mirror when possible.

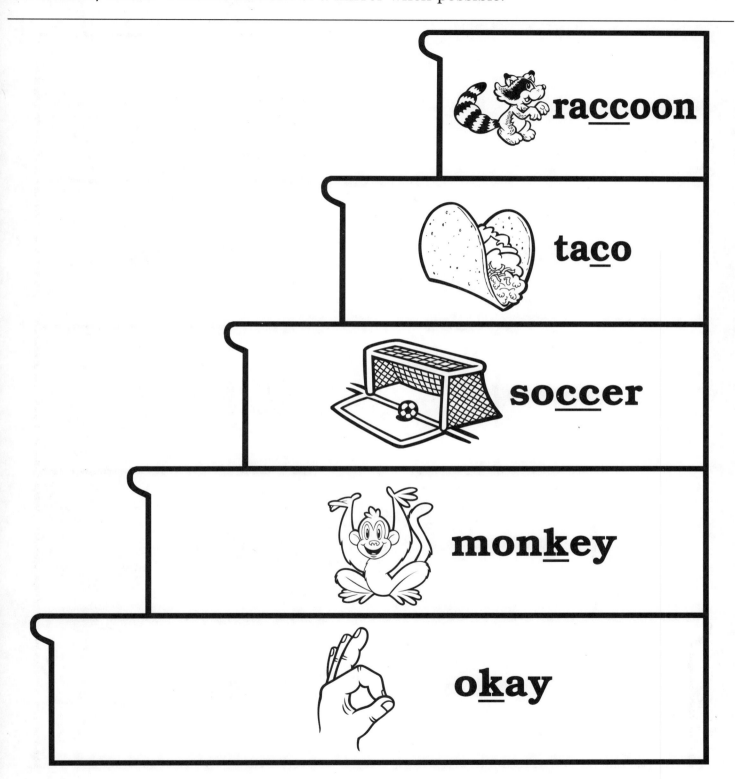

raccoon

taco

soccer

monkey

okay

**Final K
Combo Vowels**

Speech Steps

Instructions: Have the student practice saying each sound/word as he/she goes up the steps. The speech helper will read/say each sound/word. Then, have the student repeat the sounds/words. Practice in front of a mirror when possible.

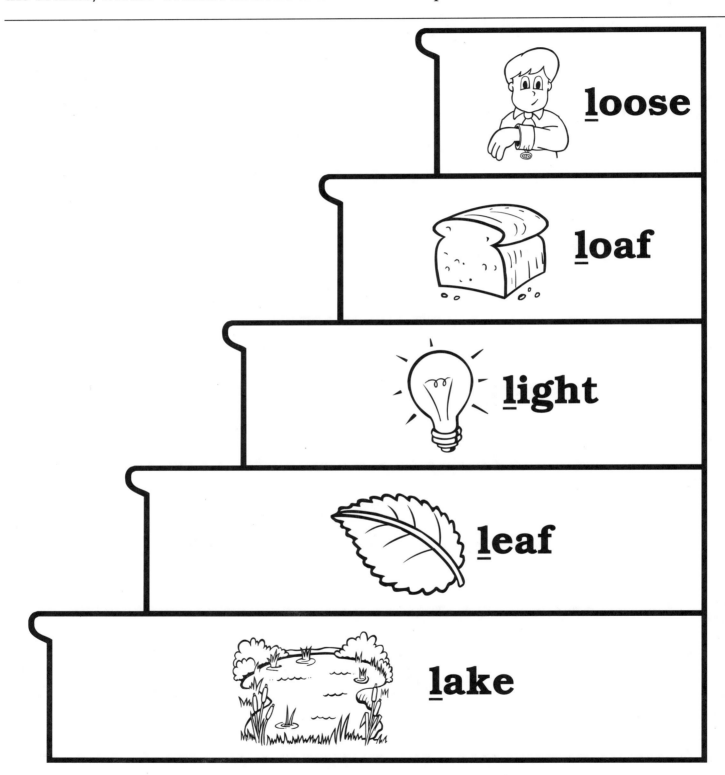

loose

loaf

light

leaf

lake

Speech Steps

Instructions: Have the student practice saying each sound/word as he/she goes up the steps. The speech helper will read/say each sound/word. Then, have the student repeat the sounds/words. Practice in front of a mirror when possible.

loop

low

line

leash

late

#BK-303 Speech Steps® • ©2002 Super Duper® Publications • 1-800-277-8737 • Online! www.superduperinc.com

Speech Steps

Instructions: Have the student practice saying each sound/word as he/she goes up the steps. The speech helper will read/say each sound/word. Then, have the student repeat the sounds/words. Practice in front of a mirror when possible.

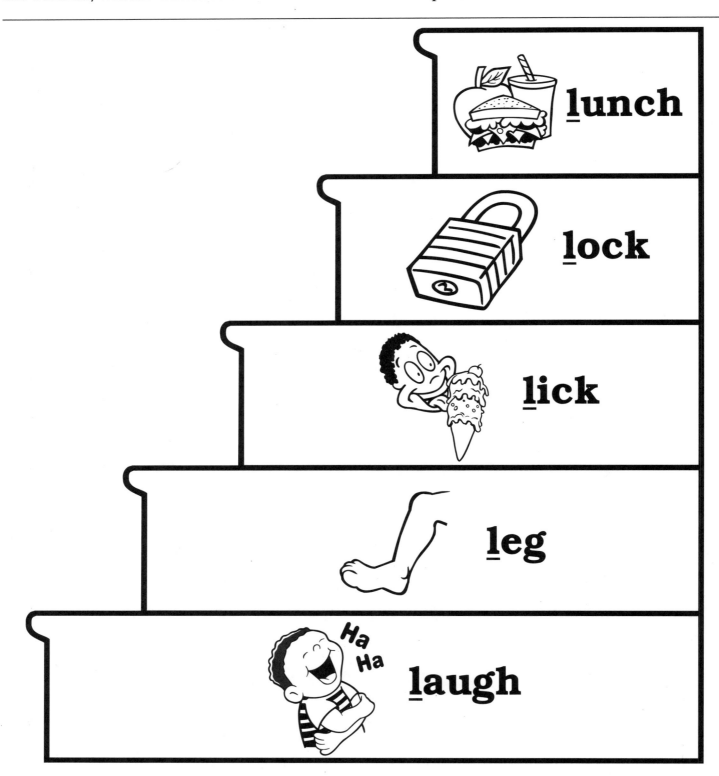

Speech Steps

Instructions: Have the student practice saying each sound/word as he/she goes up the steps. The speech helper will read/say each sound/word. Then, have the student repeat the sounds/words. Practice in front of a mirror when possible.

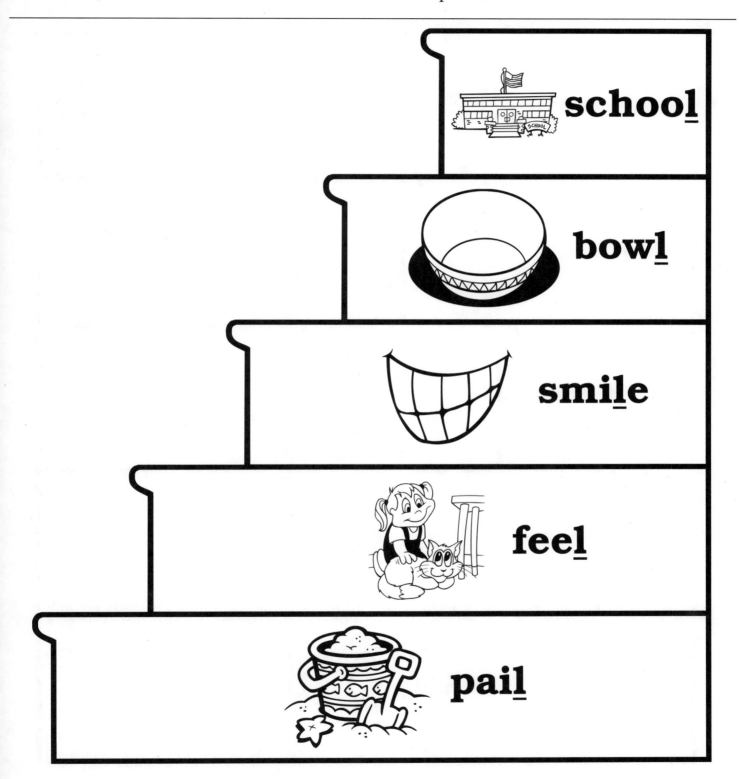

school

bowl

smile

feel

pail

#BK-303 Speech Steps® • ©2002 Super Duper® Publications • 1-800-277-8737 • Online! www.superduperinc.com

Speech Steps

Instructions: Have the student practice saying each sound/word as he/she goes up the steps. The speech helper will read/say each sound/word. Then, have the student repeat the sounds/words. Practice in front of a mirror when possible.

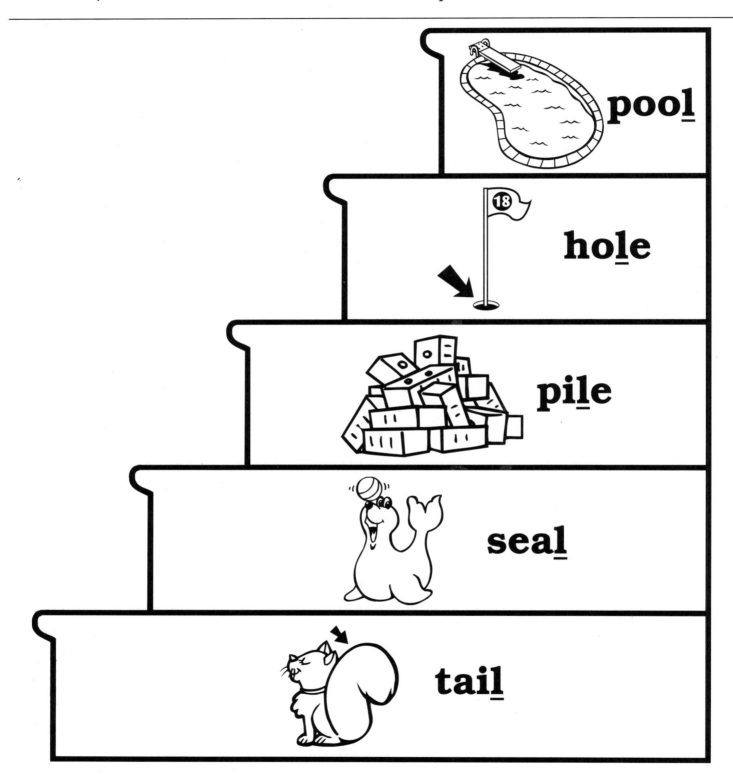

poo<u>l</u>

ho<u>l</u>e

pi<u>l</u>e

sea<u>l</u>

tai<u>l</u>

Homework Partner   Date   Name

**Final L
Long Vowels**

Speech Steps

Instructions: Have the student practice saying each sound/word as he/she goes up the steps. The speech helper will read/say each sound/word. Then, have the student repeat the sounds/words. Practice in front of a mirror when possible.

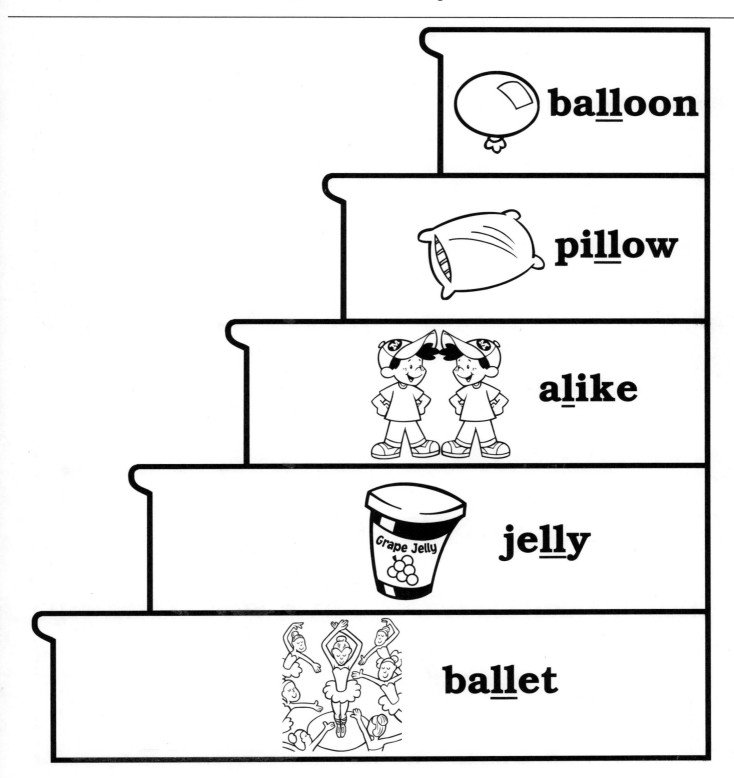

balloon

pillow

alike

jelly

ballet

Homework Partner   Date   Name

Medial L
Combo Vowels

Speech Steps

Instructions: Have the student practice saying each sound/word as he/she goes up the steps. The speech helper will read/say each sound/word. Then, have the student repeat the sounds/words. Practice in front of a mirror when possible.

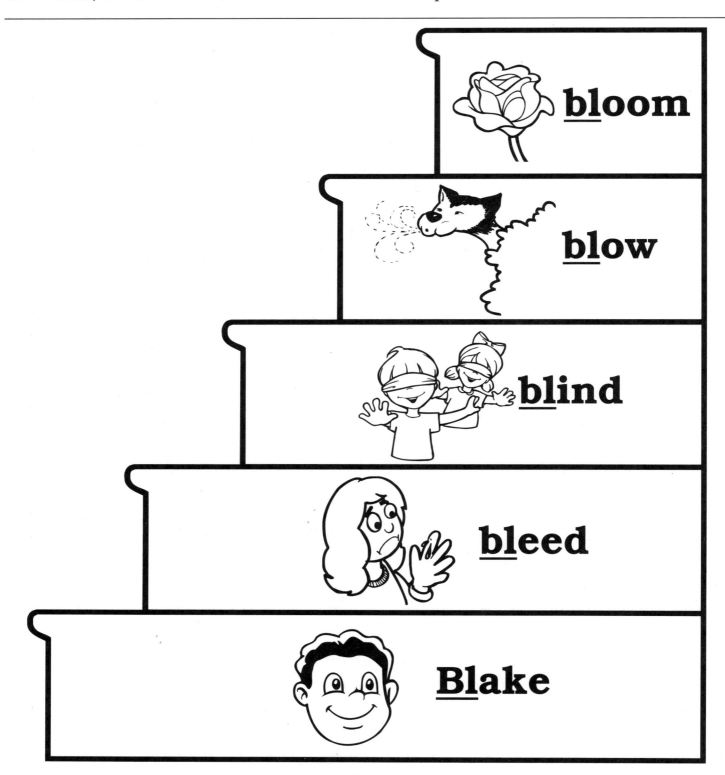

bloom

blow

blind

bleed

Blake

Speech Steps

Instructions: Have the student practice saying each sound/word as he/she goes up the steps. The speech helper will read/say each sound/word. Then, have the student repeat the sounds/words. Practice in front of a mirror when possible.

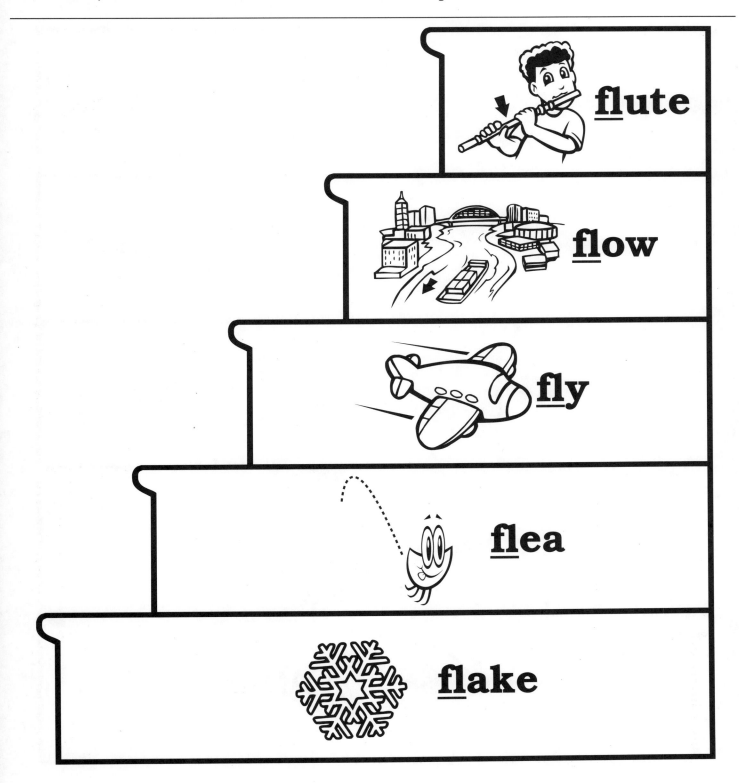

__fl__ute

__fl__ow

__fl__y

__fl__ea

__fl__ake

Homework Partner   Date   Name

Speech Steps

Instructions: Have the student practice saying each sound/word as he/she goes up the steps. The speech helper will read/say each sound/word. Then, have the student repeat the sounds/words. Practice in front of a mirror when possible.

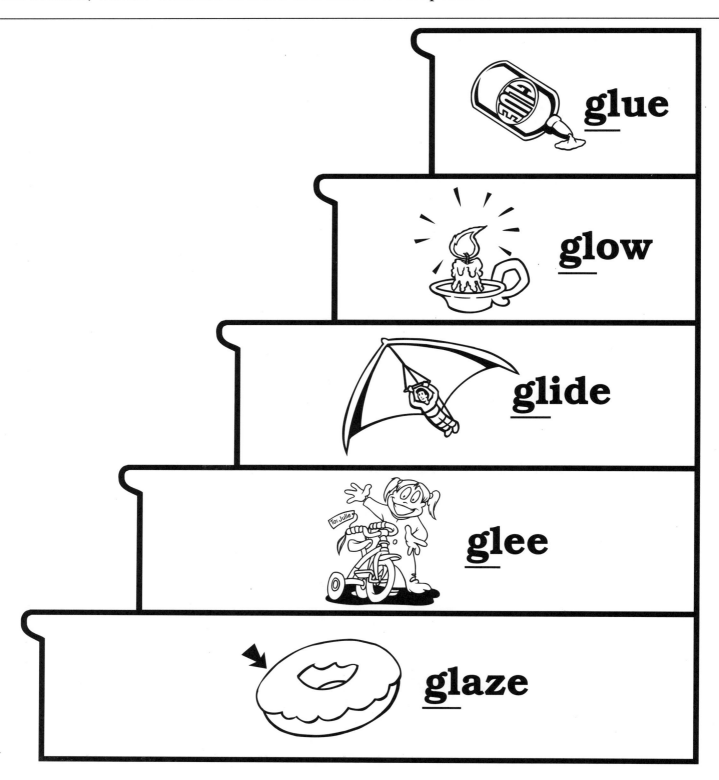

Speech Steps

Instructions: Have the student practice saying each sound/word as he/she goes up the steps. The speech helper will read/say each sound/word. Then, have the student repeat the sounds/words. Practice in front of a mirror when possible.

		<u>cl</u>ue
		<u>cl</u>ose
		<u>cl</u>imb
		<u>cl</u>ean
		<u>cl</u>ay

Homework Partner   Date   Name

L Blends
Long Vowels

Speech Steps

Instructions: Have the student practice saying each sound/word as he/she goes up the steps. The speech helper will read/say each sound/word. Then, have the student repeat the sounds/words. Practice in front of a mirror when possible.

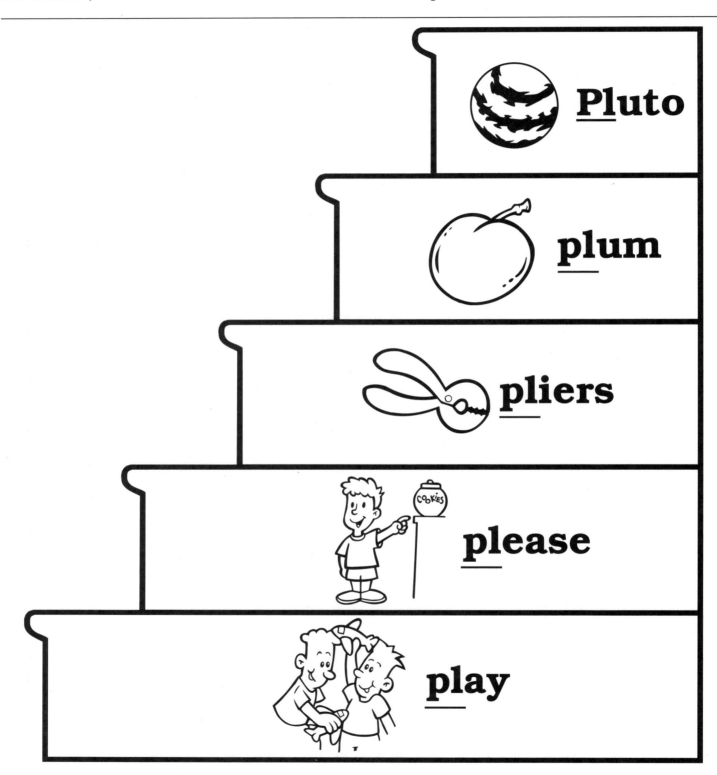

Speech Steps

Instructions: Have the student practice saying each sound/word as he/she goes up the steps. The speech helper will read/say each sound/word. Then, have the student repeat the sounds/words. Practice in front of a mirror when possible.

Speed Limit 3

sleeve

slow

slide

sleep

sleigh

Homework Partner   Date   Name

Speech Steps

Instructions: Have the student practice saying each sound/word as he/she goes up the steps. The speech helper will read/say each sound/word. Then, have the student repeat the sounds/words. Practice in front of a mirror when possible.

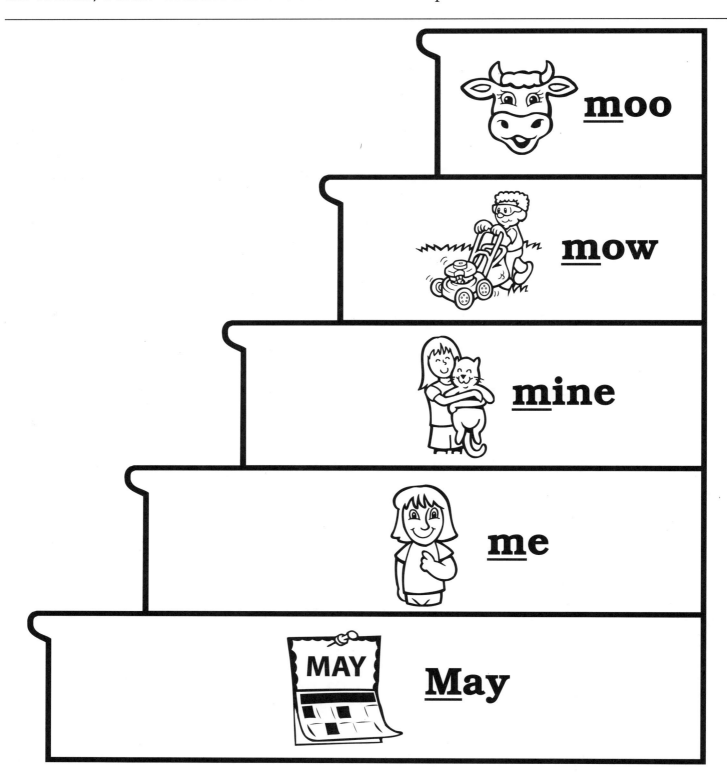

Speech Steps

Instructions: Have the student practice saying each sound/word as he/she goes up the steps. The speech helper will read/say each sound/word. Then, have the student repeat the sounds/words. Practice in front of a mirror when possible.

move

most

mice

mean

maid

Homework Partner

Date

Name

Initial M Long Vowels

Speech Steps

Instructions: Have the student practice saying each sound/word as he/she goes up the steps. The speech helper will read/say each sound/word. Then, have the student repeat the sounds/words. Practice in front of a mirror when possible.

Homework Partner   Date   Name

**Initial M
Long Vowels**

Speech Steps

Instructions: Have the student practice saying each sound/word as he/she goes up the steps. The speech helper will read/say each sound/word. Then, have the student repeat the sounds/words. Practice in front of a mirror when possible.

Speech Steps

Instructions: Have the student practice saying each sound/word as he/she goes up the steps. The speech helper will read/say each sound/word. Then, have the student repeat the sounds/words. Practice in front of a mirror when possible.

mud

mop

mitt

mess

man

Homework Partner   Date   Name

#BK-303 Speech Steps® • ©2002 Super Duper® Publications • 1-800-277-8737 • Online! www.superduperinc.com

Speech Steps

Instructions: Have the student practice saying each sound/word as he/she goes up the steps. The speech helper will read/say each sound/word. Then, have the student repeat the sounds/words. Practice in front of a mirror when possible.

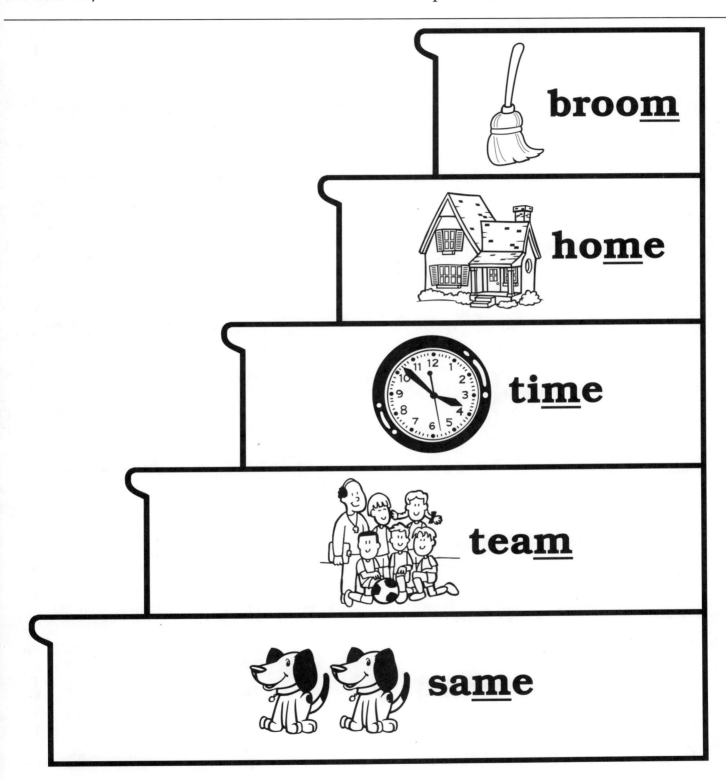

broom

home

time

team

same

#BK-303 Speech Steps® • ©2002 Super Duper® Publications • 1-800-277-8737 • Online! www.superduperinc.com

Speech Steps

Instructions: Have the student practice saying each sound/word as he/she goes up the steps. The speech helper will read/say each sound/word. Then, have the student repeat the sounds/words. Practice in front of a mirror when possible.

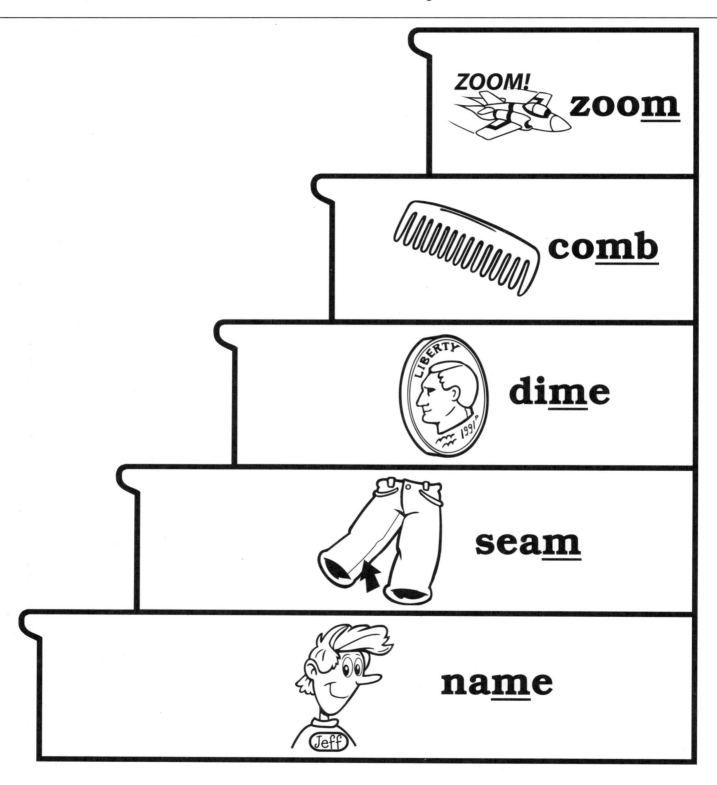

_____   _____   _____

Homework Partner   Date   Name

Final M Long Vowels

#BK-303 Speech Steps® • ©2002 Super Duper® Publications • 1-800-277-8737 • Online! www.superduperinc.com

Speech Steps

Instructions: Have the student practice saying each sound/word as he/she goes up the steps. The speech helper will read/say each sound/word. Then, have the student repeat the sounds/words. Practice in front of a mirror when possible.

re**m**ove

lawn **m**ower

re**m**ind

fla**m**ingo

to**m**ato

Homework Partner   Date   Name

**Medial M
Combo Vowels**

#BK-303 Speech Steps® • ©2002 Super Duper® Publications • 1-800-277-8737 • Online! www.superduperinc.com   77

Speech Steps

Instructions: Have the student practice saying each sound/word as he/she goes up the steps. The speech helper will read/say each sound/word. Then, have the student repeat the sounds/words. Practice in front of a mirror when possible.

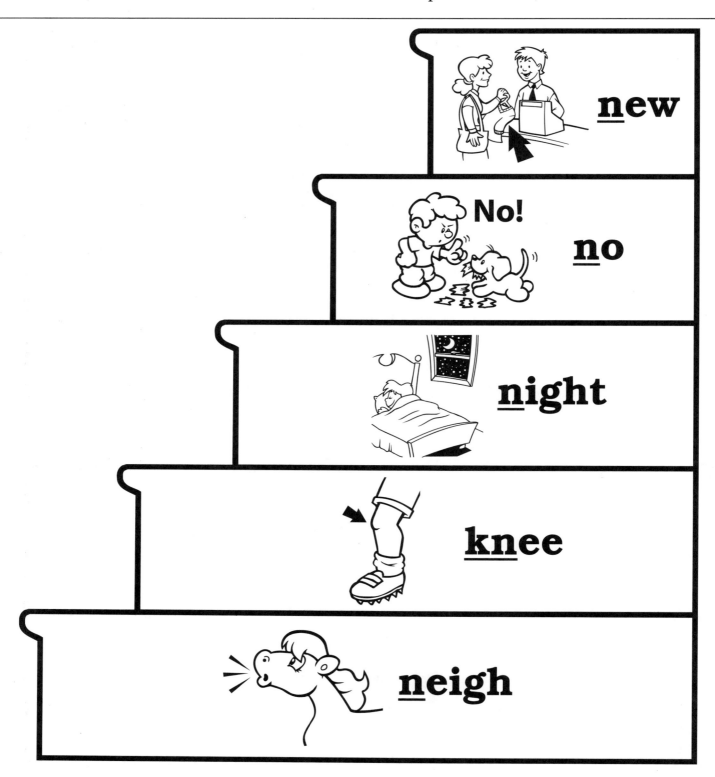

new

no

night

knee

neigh

#BK-303 Speech Steps® • ©2002 Super Duper® Publications • 1-800-277-8737 • Online! www.superduperinc.com

Speech Steps

Instructions: Have the student practice saying each sound/word as he/she goes up the steps. The speech helper will read/say each sound/word. Then, have the student repeat the sounds/words. Practice in front of a mirror when possible.

news

nose

knife

knead

name

Homework Partner   Date   Name

Speech Steps

Instructions: Have the student practice saying each sound/word as he/she goes up the steps. The speech helper will read/say each sound/word. Then, have the student repeat the sounds/words. Practice in front of a mirror when possible.

#BK-303 Speech Steps® • ©2002 Super Duper® Publications • 1-800-277-8737 • Online! www.superduperinc.com

Speech Steps

Instructions: Have the student practice saying each sound/word as he/she goes up the steps. The speech helper will read/say each sound/word. Then, have the student repeat the sounds/words. Practice in front of a mirror when possible.

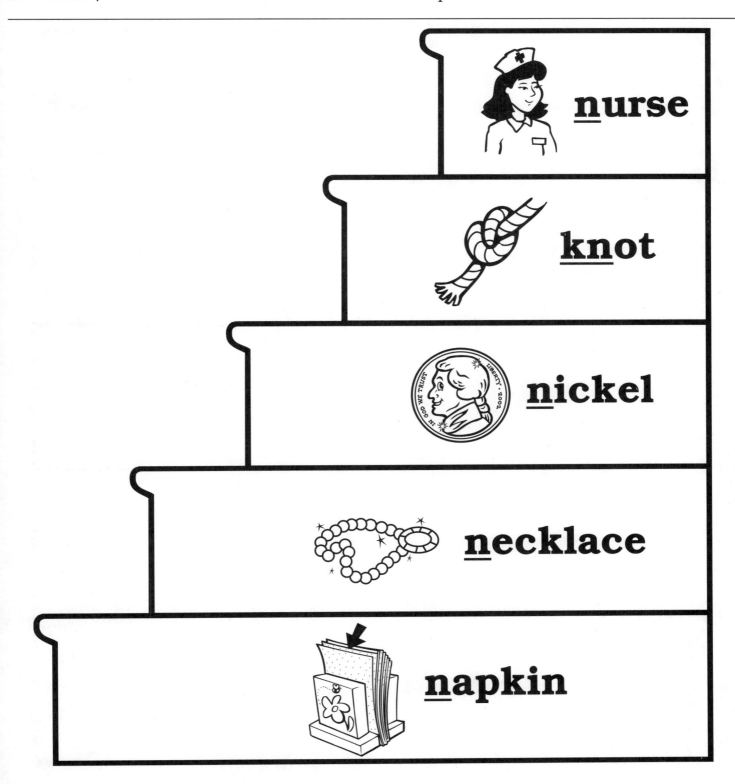

nurse

knot

nickel

necklace

napkin

Homework Partner

Date

Name

**Initial N
Short Vowels**

#BK-303 Speech Steps® • ©2002 Super Duper® Publications • 1-800-277-8737 • Online! www.superduperinc.com

81

Speech Steps

Instructions: Have the student practice saying each sound/word as he/she goes up the steps. The speech helper will read/say each sound/word. Then, have the student repeat the sounds/words. Practice in front of a mirror when possible.

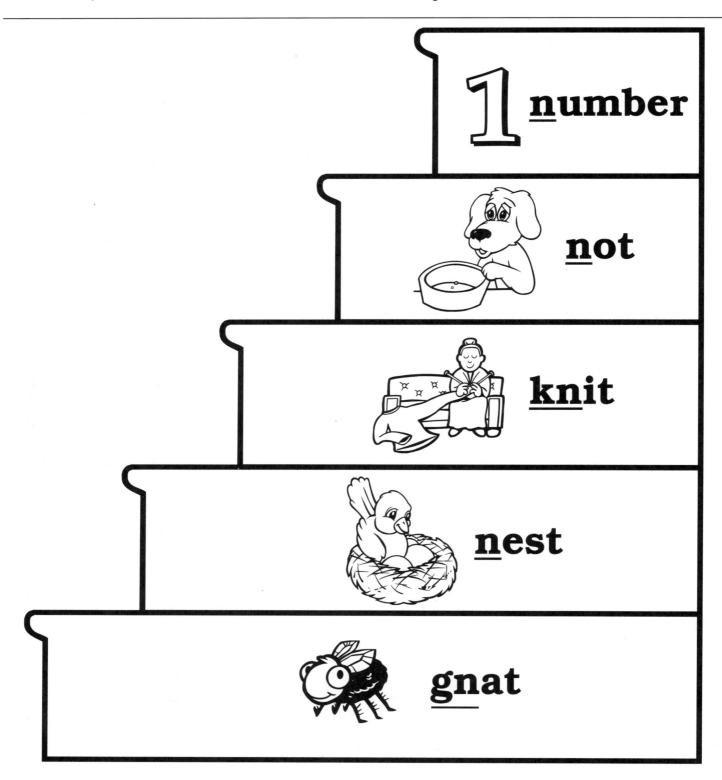

1 <u>n</u>umber

<u>n</u>ot

<u>kn</u>it

<u>n</u>est

<u>gn</u>at

Homework Partner   Date   Name

Initial N
Short Vowels

#BK-303 Speech Steps® • ©2002 Super Duper® Publications • 1-800-277-8737 • Online! www.superduperinc.com

Speech Steps

Instructions: Have the student practice saying each sound/word as he/she goes up the steps. The speech helper will read/say each sound/word. Then, have the student repeat the sounds/words. Practice in front of a mirror when possible.

spoon

phone

9 nine

queen

rain

**Final N
Long Vowels**

Speech Steps

Instructions: Have the student practice saying each sound/word as he/she goes up the steps. The speech helper will read/say each sound/word. Then, have the student repeat the sounds/words. Practice in front of a mirror when possible.

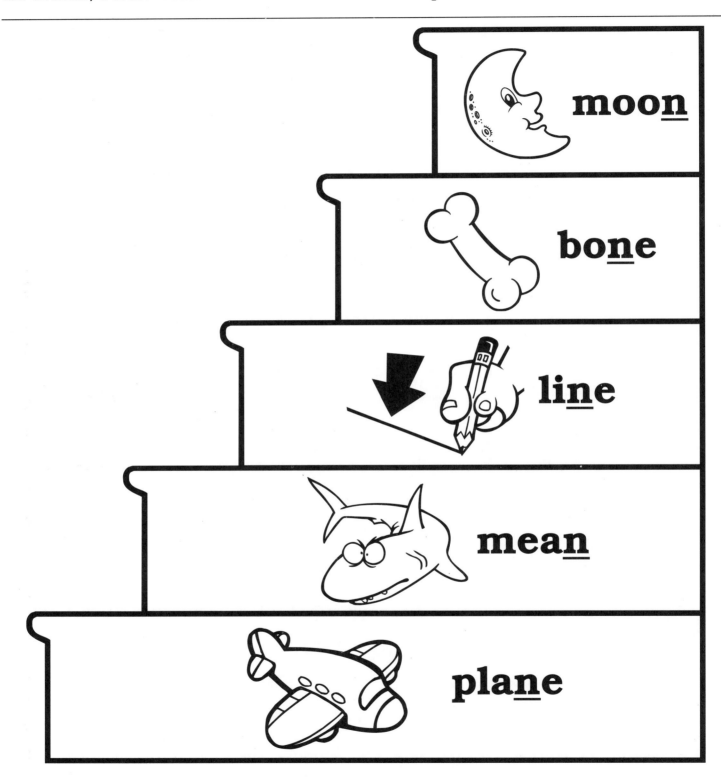

moon

bone

line

mean

plane

Final N Long Vowels

#BK-303 Speech Steps® • ©2002 Super Duper® Publications • 1-800-277-8737 • Online! www.superduperinc.com

Speech Steps

Instructions: Have the student practice saying each sound/word as he/she goes up the steps. The speech helper will read/say each sound/word. Then, have the student repeat the sounds/words. Practice in front of a mirror when possible.

peanut

dinosaur

animal

bunny

banana

**Medial N
Combo Vowels**

Speech Steps

Instructions: Have the student practice saying each sound/word as he/she goes up the steps. The speech helper will read/say each sound/word. Then, have the student repeat the sounds/words. Practice in front of a mirror when possible.

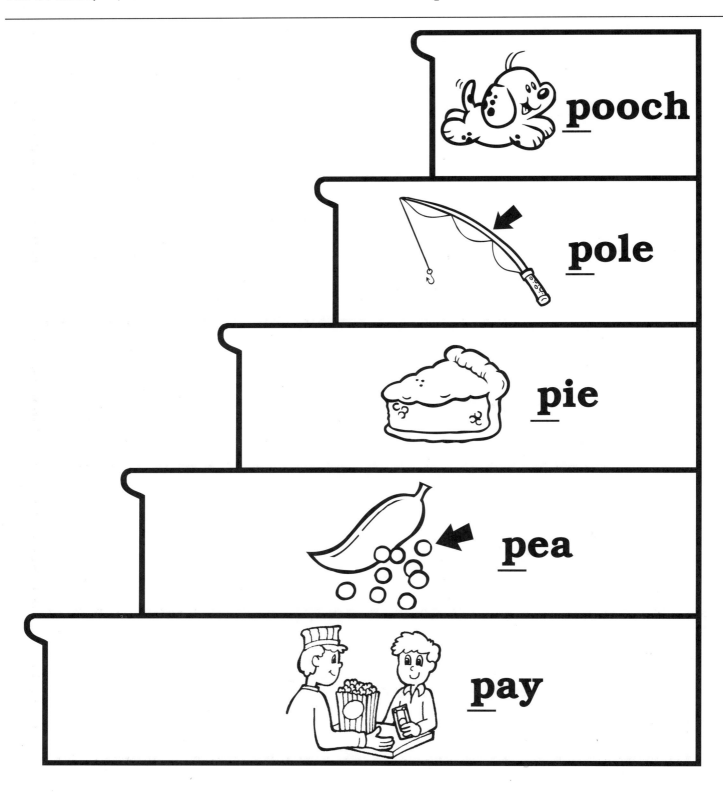

pooch

pole

pie

pea

pay

Speech Steps

Instructions: Have the student practice saying each sound/word as he/she goes up the steps. The speech helper will read/say each sound/word. Then, have the student repeat the sounds/words. Practice in front of a mirror when possible.

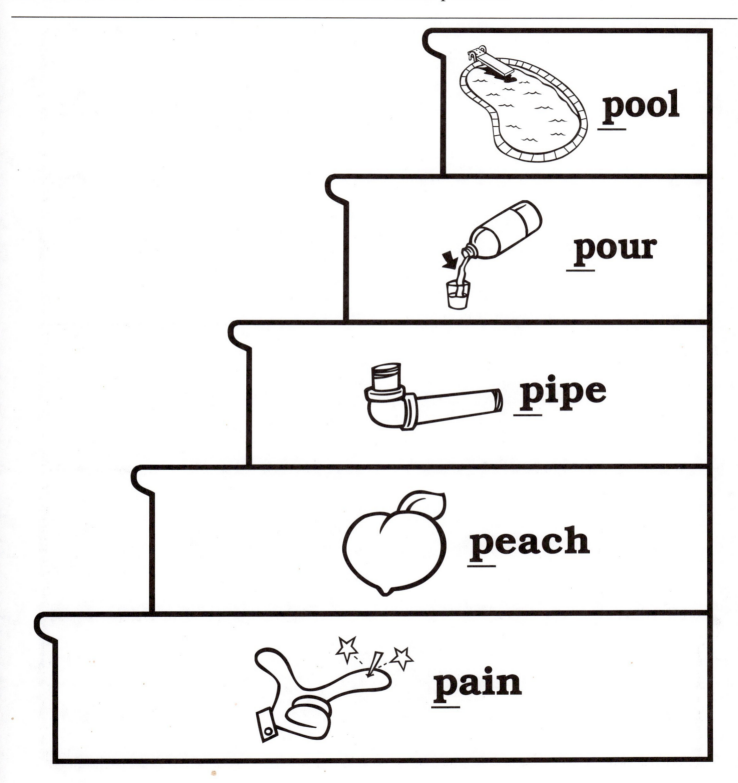

pool

pour

pipe

peach

pain

Speech Steps

Instructions: Have the student practice saying each sound/word as he/she goes up the steps. The speech helper will read/say each sound/word. Then, have the student repeat the sounds/words. Practice in front of a mirror when possible.

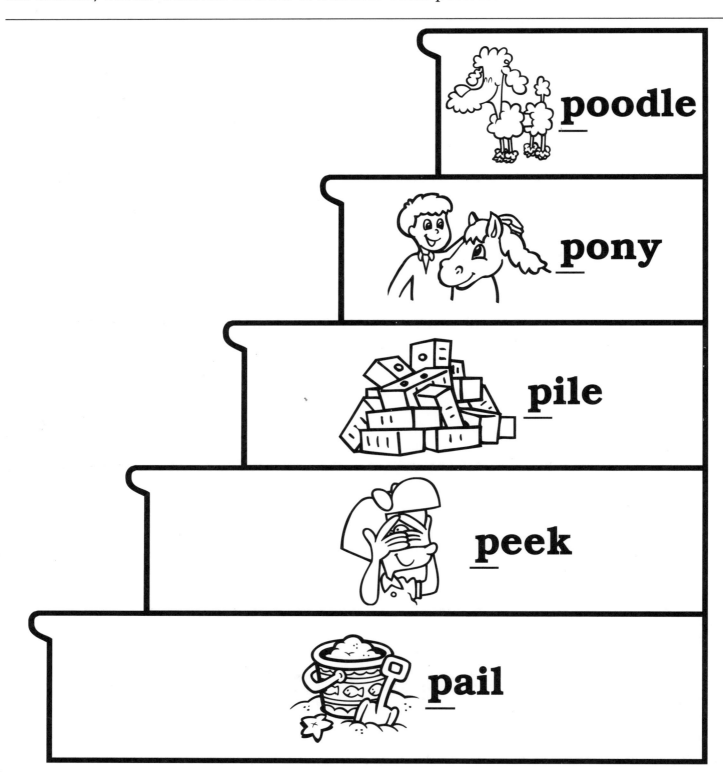

poodle

pony

pile

peek

pail

#BK-303 Speech Steps® • ©2002 Super Duper® Publications • 1-800-277-8737 • Online! www.superduperinc.com

Speech Steps

Instructions: Have the student practice saying each sound/word as he/she goes up the steps. The speech helper will read/say each sound/word. Then, have the student repeat the sounds/words. Practice in front of a mirror when possible.

Speech Steps

Instructions: Have the student practice saying each sound/word as he/she goes up the steps. The speech helper will read/say each sound/word. Then, have the student repeat the sounds/words. Practice in front of a mirror when possible.

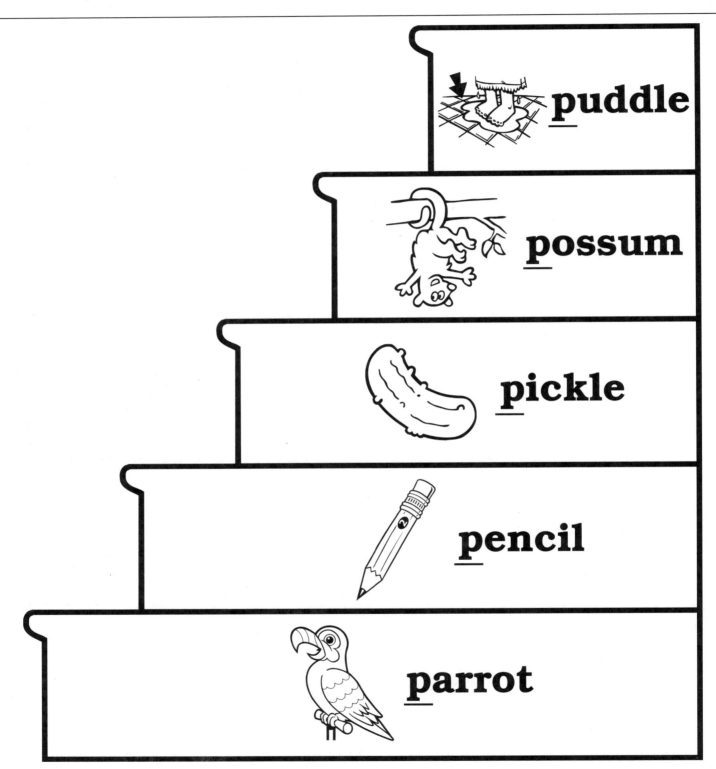

puddle

possum

pickle

pencil

parrot

Homework Partner   Date   Name

#BK-303 Speech Steps® • ©2002 Super Duper® Publications • 1-800-277-8737 • Online! www.superduperinc.com

Speech Steps

Instructions: Have the student practice saying each sound/word as he/she goes up the steps. The speech helper will read/say each sound/word. Then, have the student repeat the sounds/words. Practice in front of a mirror when possible.

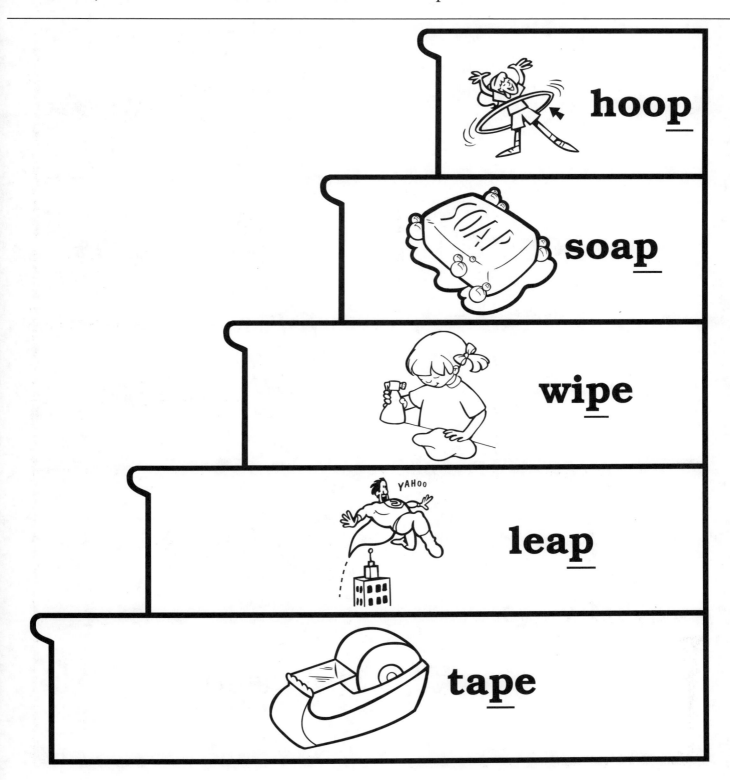

hoo**p**

soa**p**

wi**p**e

lea**p**

ta**p**e

Speech Steps

Instructions: Have the student practice saying each sound/word as he/she goes up the steps. The speech helper will read/say each sound/word. Then, have the student repeat the sounds/words. Practice in front of a mirror when possible.

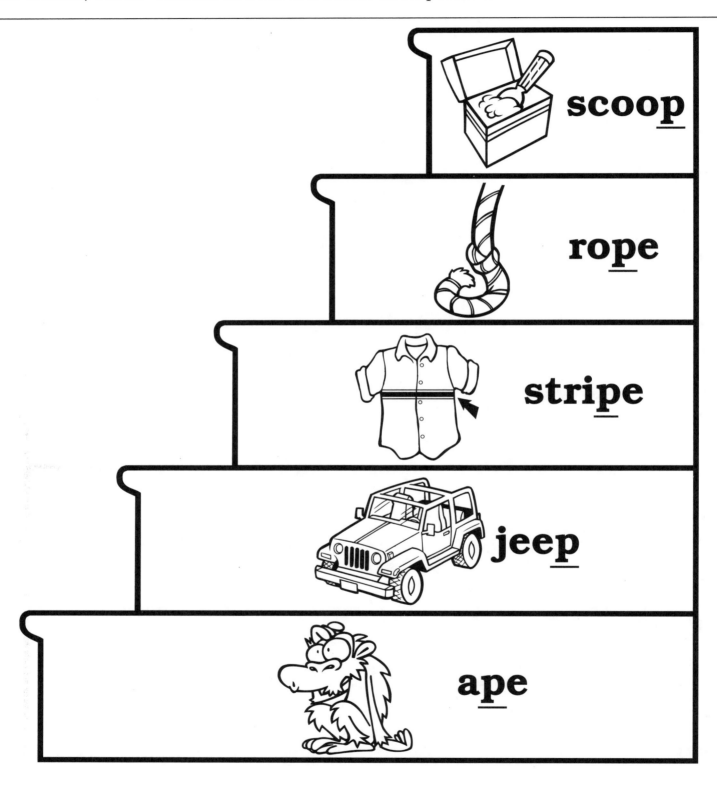

scoop

rope

stripe

jeep

ape

Speech Steps

Instructions: Have the student practice saying each sound/word as he/she goes up the steps. The speech helper will read/say each sound/word. Then, have the student repeat the sounds/words. Practice in front of a mirror when possible.

shampoo

hippo

open

teepee

wallpaper

Homework Partner   Date   Name

Medial P Combo Vowels

Speech Steps

Instructions: Have the student practice saying each sound/word as he/she goes up the steps. The speech helper will read/say each sound/word. Then, have the student repeat the sounds/words. Practice in front of a mirror when possible.

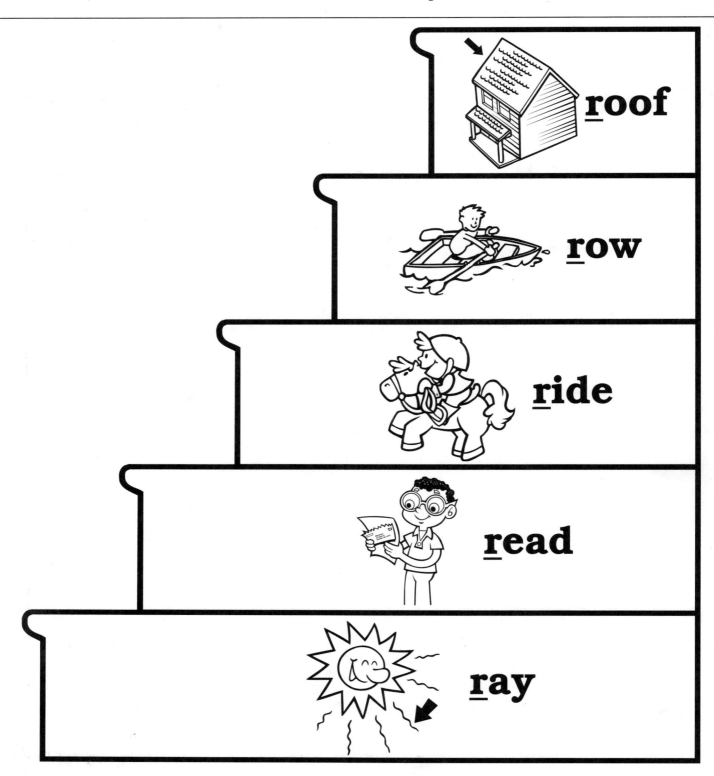

roof

row

ride

read

ray

#BK-303 Speech Steps® • ©2002 Super Duper® Publications • 1-800-277-8737 • Online! www.superduperinc.com

Speech Steps

Instructions: Have the student practice saying each sound/word as he/she goes up the steps. The speech helper will read/say each sound/word. Then, have the student repeat the sounds/words. Practice in front of a mirror when possible.

<u>r</u>oom

<u>r</u>ose

<u>wr</u>ite

<u>r</u>eel

<u>r</u>ain

Homework Partner   Date   Name

Speech Steps

Instructions: Have the student practice saying each sound/word as he/she goes up the steps. The speech helper will read/say each sound/word. Then, have the student repeat the sounds/words. Practice in front of a mirror when possible.

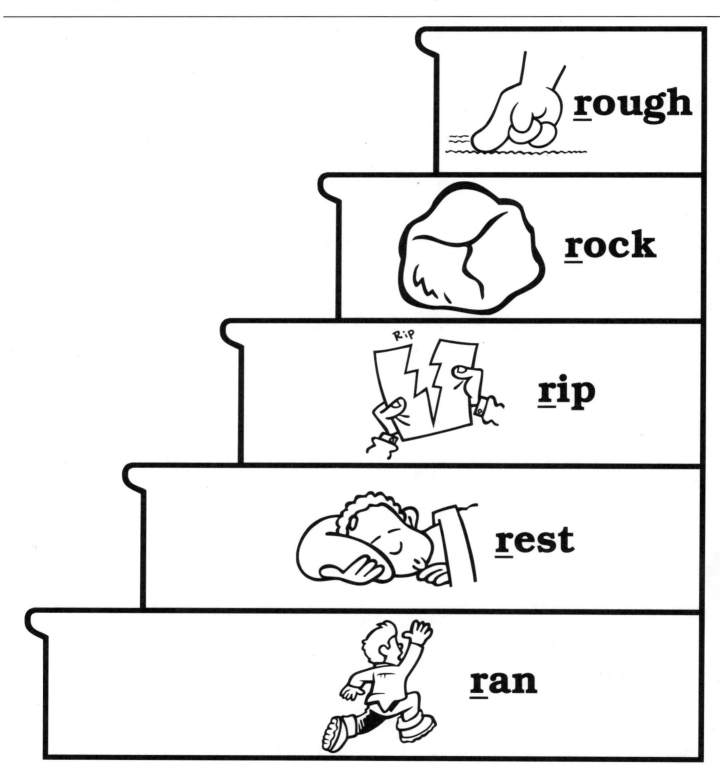

__r__ough

__r__ock

__r__ip

__r__est

__r__an

Initial R Short Vowels

#BK-303 Speech Steps® • ©2002 Super Duper® Publications • 1-800-277-8737 • Online! www.superduperinc.com

Speech Steps

Instructions: Have the student practice saying each sound/word as he/she goes up the steps. The speech helper will read/say each sound/word. Then, have the student repeat the sounds/words. Practice in front of a mirror when possible.

Homework Partner   Date   Name

Speech Steps

Instructions: Have the student practice saying each sound/word as he/she goes up the steps. The speech helper will read/say each sound/word. Then, have the student repeat the sounds/words. Practice in front of a mirror when possible.

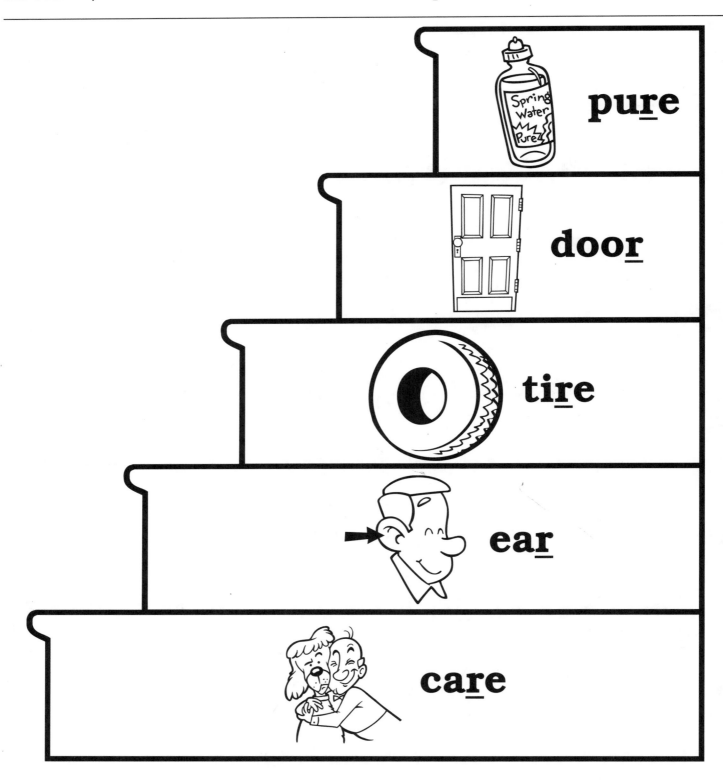

pure

door

tire

ear

care

Speech Steps

Instructions: Have the student practice saying each sound/word as he/she goes up the steps. The speech helper will read/say each sound/word. Then, have the student repeat the sounds/words. Practice in front of a mirror when possible.

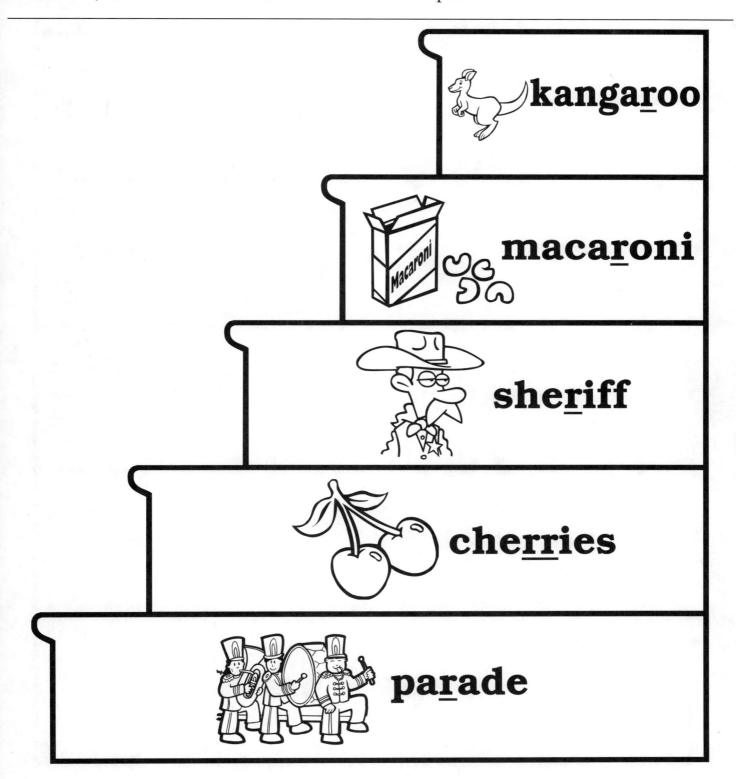

Homework Partner   Date   Name

Medial R Combo Vowels

Speech Steps

Instructions: Have the student practice saying each sound/word as he/she goes up the steps. The speech helper will read/say each sound/word. Then, have the student repeat the sounds/words. Practice in front of a mirror when possible.

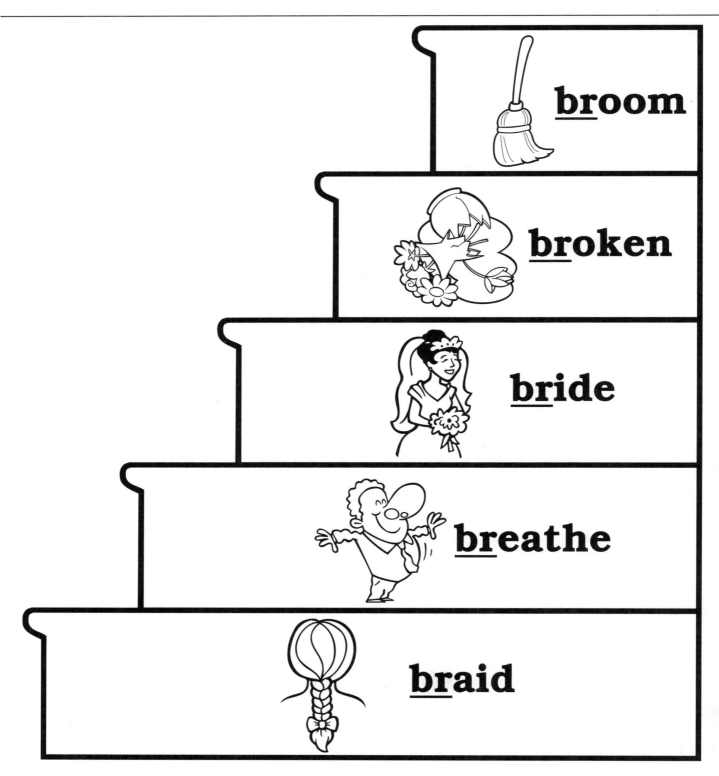

broom

broken

bride

breathe

braid

R Blends
Long Vowels

Speech Steps

Instructions: Have the student practice saying each sound/word as he/she goes up the steps. The speech helper will read/say each sound/word. Then, have the student repeat the sounds/words. Practice in front of a mirror when possible.

drew

drove

dry

dream

drain

Homework Partner   Date   Name

**R Blends
Long Vowels**

Speech Steps

Instructions: Have the student practice saying each sound/word as he/she goes up the steps. The speech helper will read/say each sound/word. Then, have the student repeat the sounds/words. Practice in front of a mirror when possible.

fruit

froze

fry

freeze

frame

Speech Steps

Instructions: Have the student practice saying each sound/word as he/she goes up the steps. The speech helper will read/say each sound/word. Then, have the student repeat the sounds/words. Practice in front of a mirror when possible.

grew

grow

grimy

green

grapes

Homework Partner   Date   Name

R Blends
Long Vowels

Speech Steps

Instructions: Have the student practice saying each sound/word as he/she goes up the steps. The speech helper will read/say each sound/word. Then, have the student repeat the sounds/words. Practice in front of a mirror when possible.

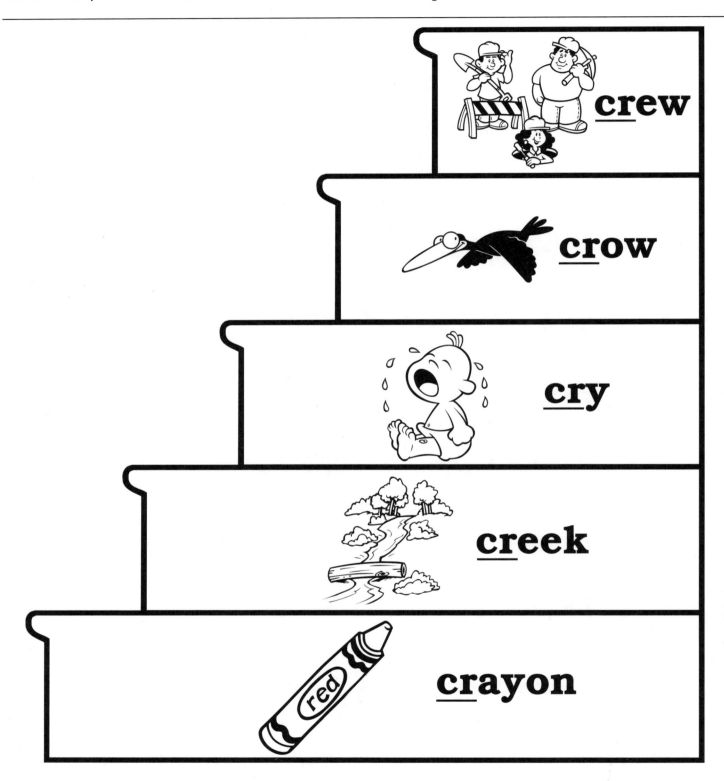

crew

crow

cry

creek

crayon

Speech Steps

Instructions: Have the student practice saying each sound/word as he/she goes up the steps. The speech helper will read/say each sound/word. Then, have the student repeat the sounds/words. Practice in front of a mirror when possible.

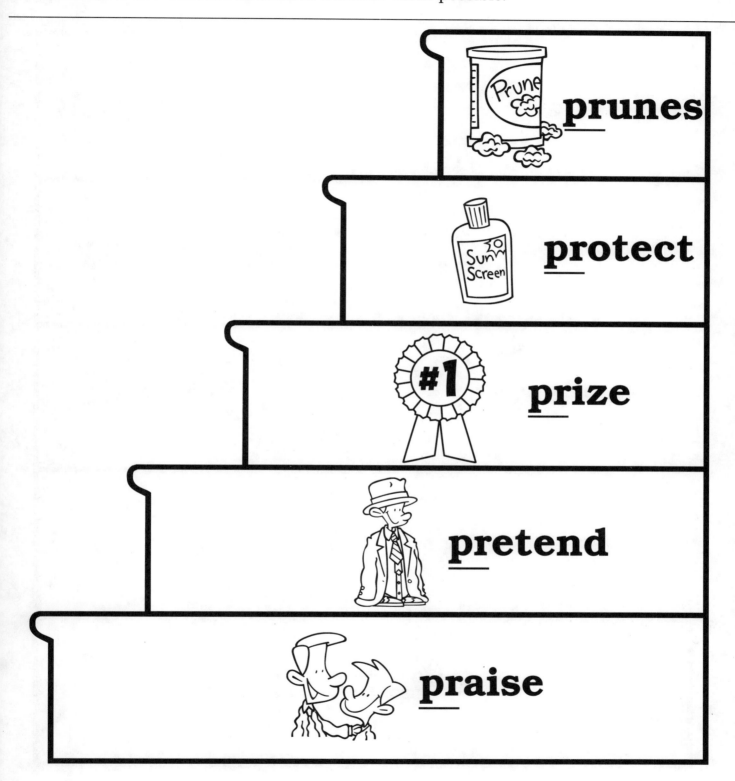

Homework Partner   Date   Name

**R Blends
Long Vowels**

Speech Steps

Instructions: Have the student practice saying each sound/word as he/she goes up the steps. The speech helper will read/say each sound/word. Then, have the student repeat the sounds/words. Practice in front of a mirror when possible.

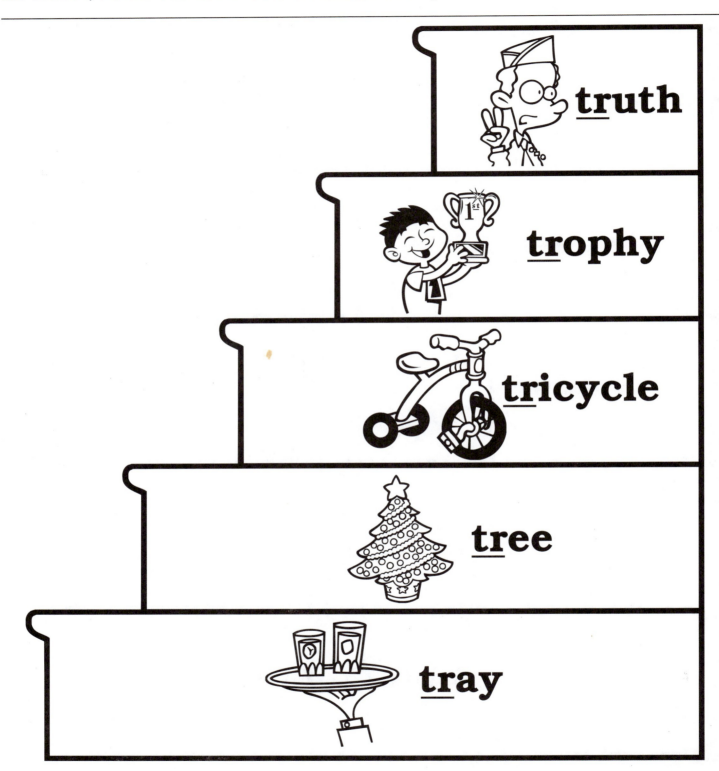

truth

trophy

tricycle

tree

tray

Speech Steps

Instructions: Have the student practice saying each sound/word as he/she goes up the steps. The speech helper will read/say each sound/word. Then, have the student repeat the sounds/words. Practice in front of a mirror when possible.

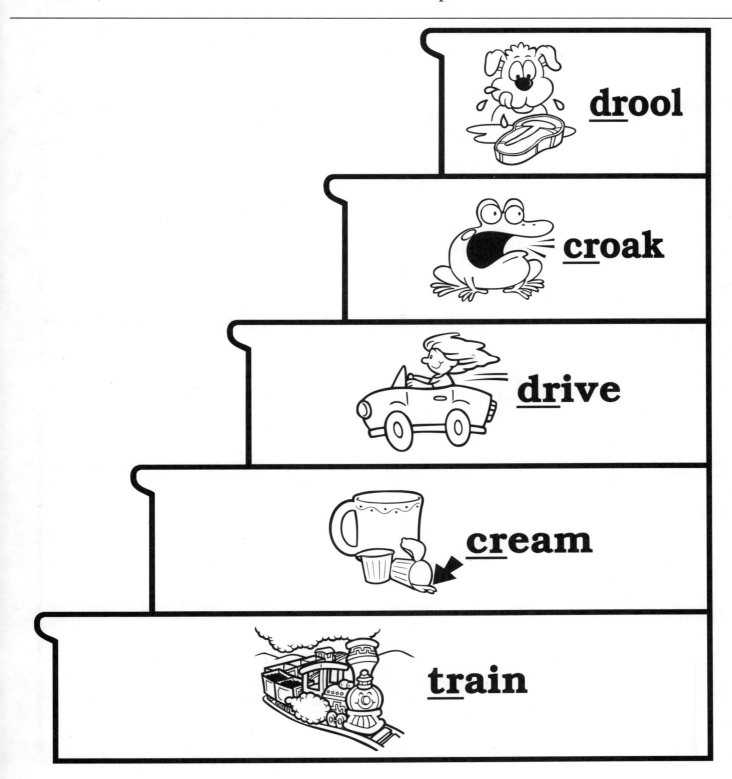

drool

croak

drive

cream

train

Speech Steps

Instructions: Have the student practice saying each sound/word as he/she goes up the steps. The speech helper will read/say each sound/word. Then, have the student repeat the sounds/words. Practice in front of a mirror when possible.

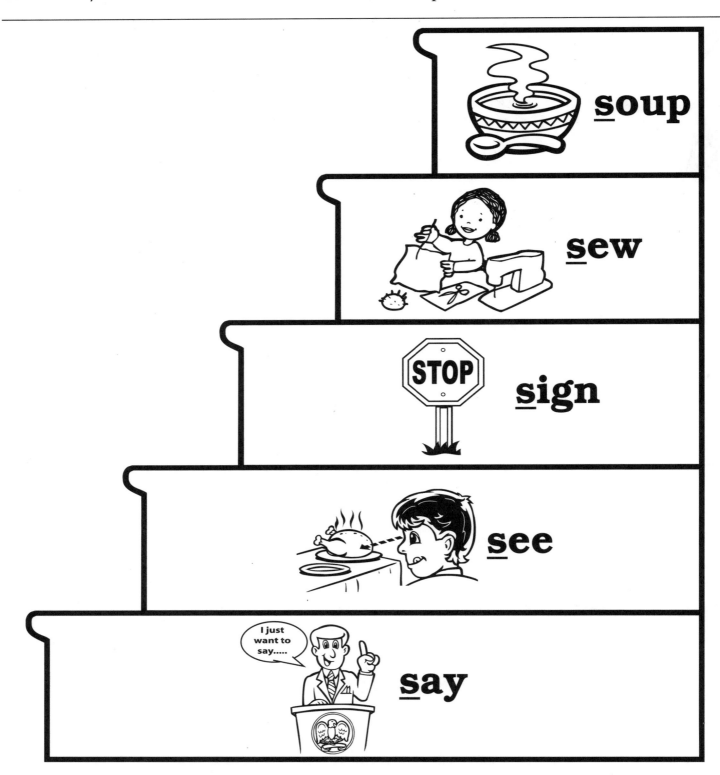

**Initial S
Long Vowels**

#BK-303 Speech Steps® • ©2002 Super Duper® Publications • 1-800-277-8737 • Online! www.superduperinc.com

Speech Steps

Instructions: Have the student practice saying each sound/word as he/she goes up the steps. The speech helper will read/say each sound/word. Then, have the student repeat the sounds/words. Practice in front of a mirror when possible.

suit

soap

side

seat

same

Homework Partner   Date   Name   **Initial S Long Vowels**

#BK-303 Speech Steps® • ©2002 Super Duper® Publications • 1-800-277-8737 • Online! www.superduperinc.com   109

Speech Steps

Instructions: Have the student practice saying each sound/word as he/she goes up the steps. The speech helper will read/say each sound/word. Then, have the student repeat the sounds/words. Practice in front of a mirror when possible.

__s__un

__s__ock

__s__it

__s__ell

__s__ad

Homework Partner   Date   Name

Initial S Short Vowels

#BK-303 Speech Steps® • ©2002 Super Duper® Publications • 1-800-277-8737 • Online! www.superduperinc.com

Speech Steps

Instructions: Have the student practice saying each sound/word as he/she goes up the steps. The speech helper will read/say each sound/word. Then, have the student repeat the sounds/words. Practice in front of a mirror when possible.

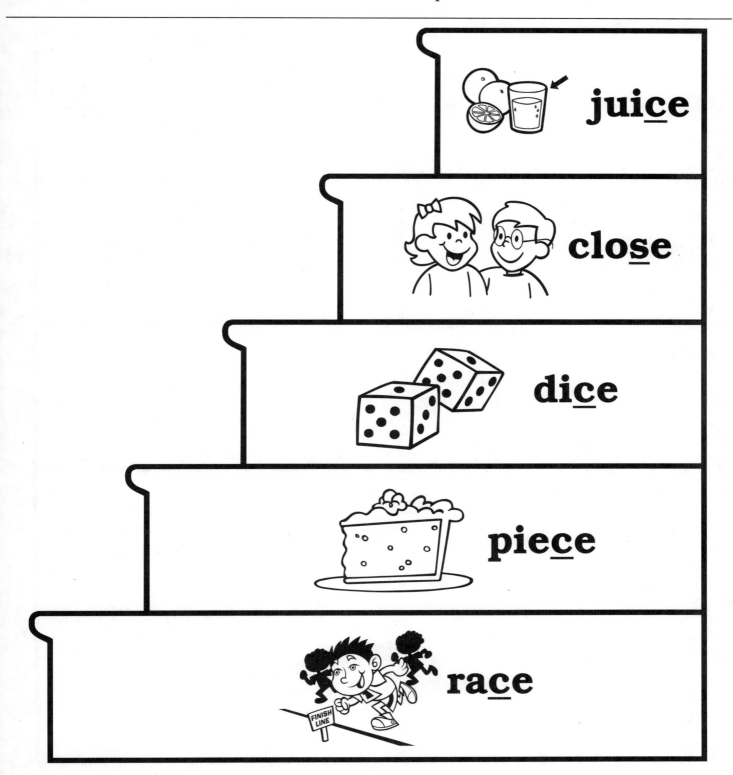

juice

close

dice

piece

race

Speech Steps

Instructions: Have the student practice saying each sound/word as he/she goes up the steps. The speech helper will read/say each sound/word. Then, have the student repeat the sounds/words. Practice in front of a mirror when possible.

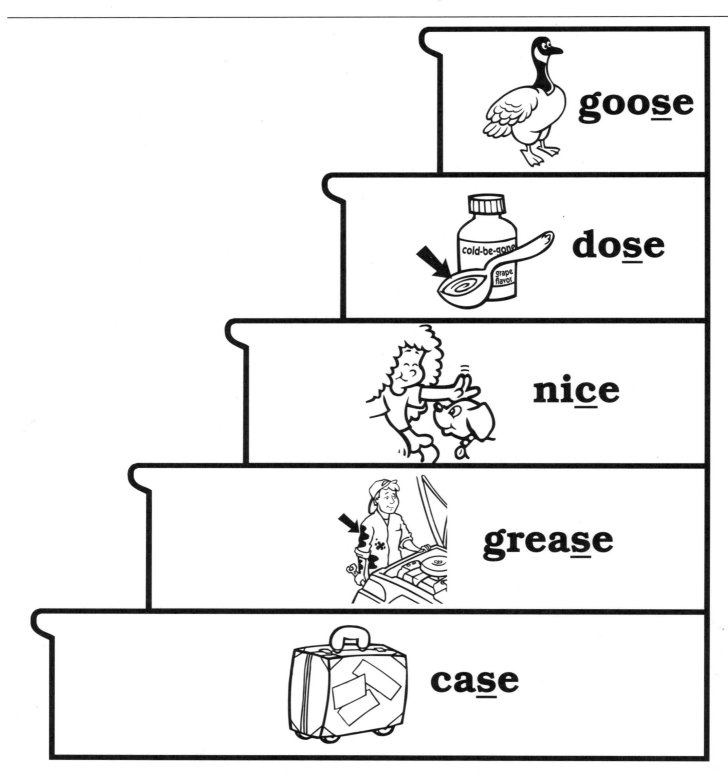

goose

dose

nice

grease

case

Final S Long Vowels

#BK-303 Speech Steps® • ©2002 Super Duper® Publications • 1-800-277-8737 • Online! www.superduperinc.com

Speech Steps

Instructions: Have the student practice saying each sound/word as he/she goes up the steps. The speech helper will read/say each sound/word. Then, have the student repeat the sounds/words. Practice in front of a mirror when possible.

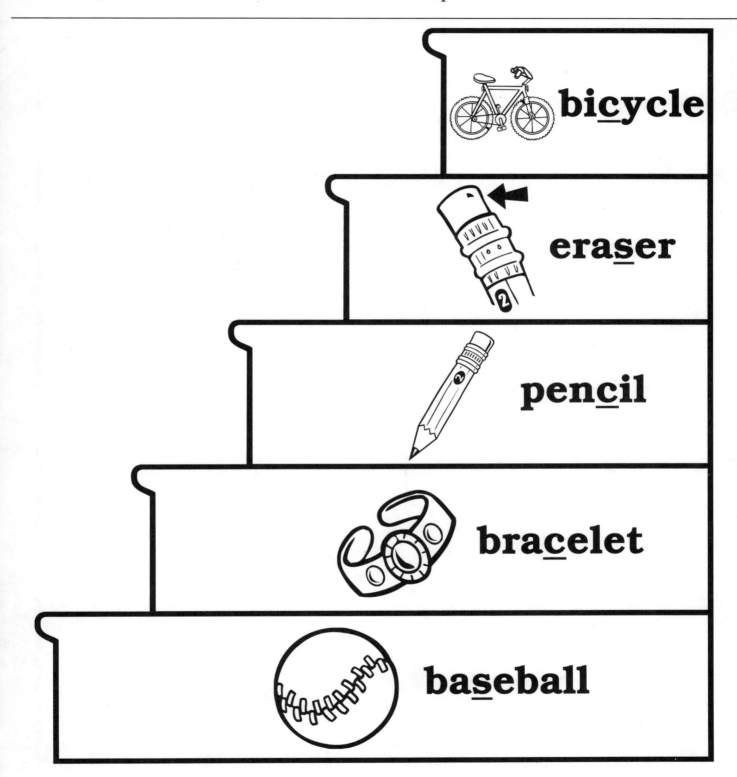

bicycle

eraser

pencil

bracelet

baseball

Homework Partner   Date   Name

Speech Steps

Instructions: Have the student practice saying each sound/word as he/she goes up the steps. The speech helper will read/say each sound/word. Then, have the student repeat the sounds/words. Practice in front of a mirror when possible.

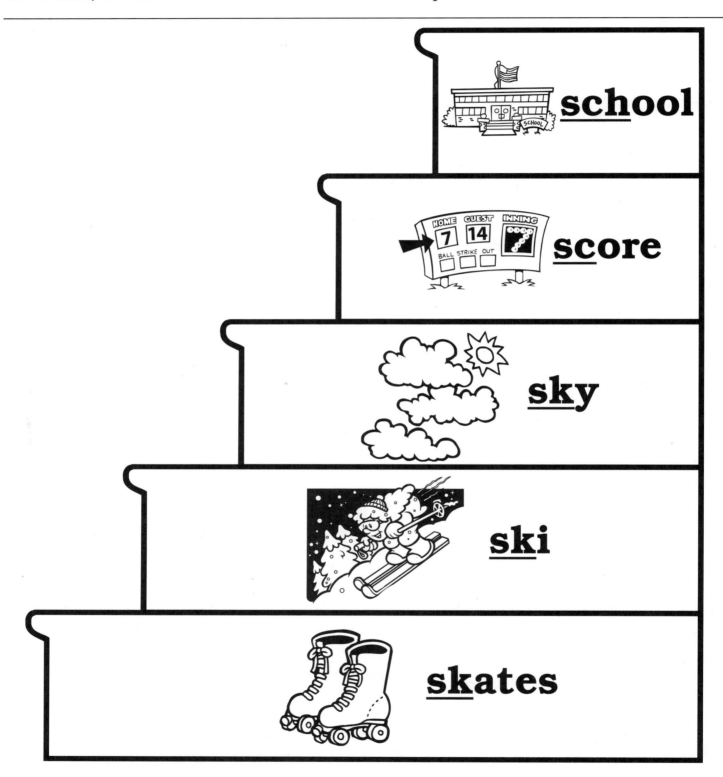

school

score

sky

ski

skates

S Blends Long Vowels

#BK-303 Speech Steps® • ©2002 Super Duper® Publications • 1-800-277-8737 • Online! www.superduperinc.com

Speech Steps

Instructions: Have the student practice saying each sound/word as he/she goes up the steps. The speech helper will read/say each sound/word. Then, have the student repeat the sounds/words. Practice in front of a mirror when possible.

#BK-303 Speech Steps® • ©2002 Super Duper® Publications • 1-800-277-8737 • Online! www.superduperinc.com

Speech Steps

Instructions: Have the student practice saying each sound/word as he/she goes up the steps. The speech helper will read/say each sound/word. Then, have the student repeat the sounds/words. Practice in front of a mirror when possible.

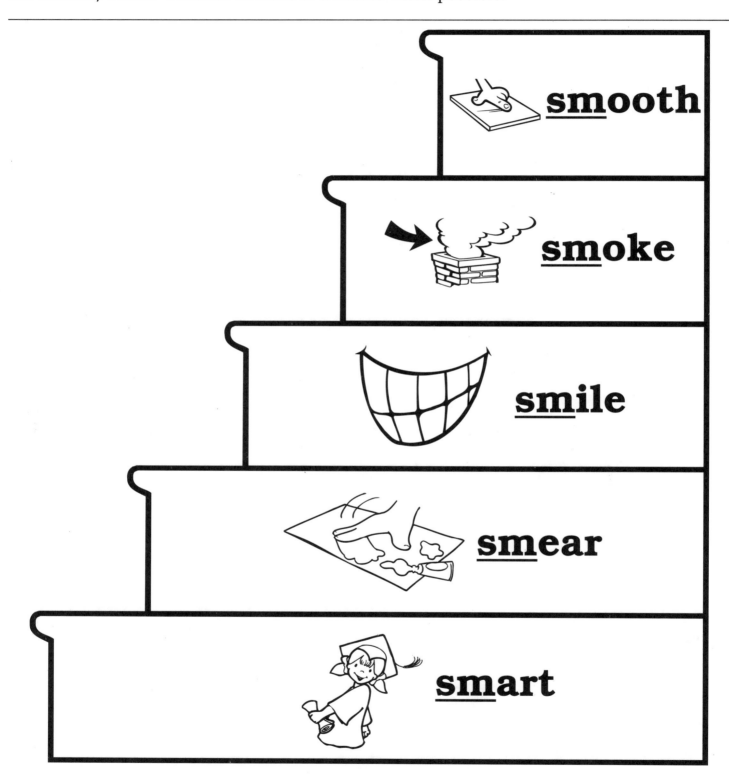

smooth

smoke

smile

smear

smart

Homework Partner   Date   Name

**S Blends
Combo Vowels**

116   #BK-303 Speech Steps® • ©2002 Super Duper® Publications • 1-800-277-8737 • Online! www.superduperinc.com

Speech Steps

Instructions: Have the student practice saying each sound/word as he/she goes up the steps. The speech helper will read/say each sound/word. Then, have the student repeat the sounds/words. Practice in front of a mirror when possible.

snooze

snow

sniff

sneeze

snake

Homework Partner

Date

Name

S Blends Combo Vowels

Speech Steps

Instructions: Have the student practice saying each sound/word as he/she goes up the steps. The speech helper will read/say each sound/word. Then, have the student repeat the sounds/words. Practice in front of a mirror when possible.

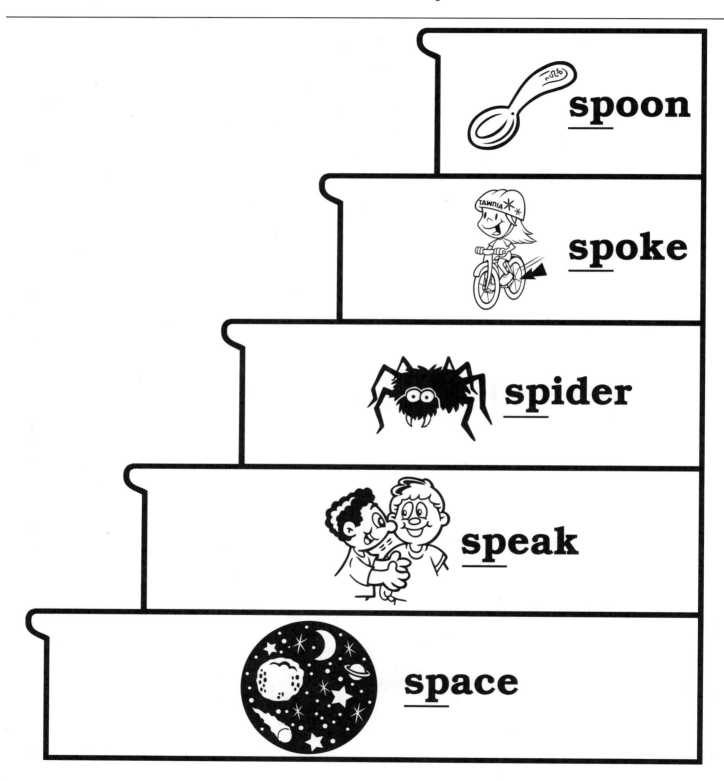

Speech Steps

Instructions: Have the student practice saying each sound/word as he/she goes up the steps. The speech helper will read/say each sound/word. Then, have the student repeat the sounds/words. Practice in front of a mirror when possible.

<u>st</u>ool

<u>st</u>one

<u>st</u>yle

<u>st</u>eam

<u>st</u>eak

| Homework Partner | Date | Name | **S Blends Long Vowels** |

Speech Steps

Instructions: Have the student practice saying each sound/word as he/she goes up the steps. The speech helper will read/say each sound/word. Then, have the student repeat the sounds/words. Practice in front of a mirror when possible.

swoop

sworn

swipe

sweep

sway

Homework Partner   Date   Name

S Blends Long Vowels

#BK-303 Speech Steps® • ©2002 Super Duper® Publications • 1-800-277-8737 • Online! www.superduperinc.com

Speech Steps

Instructions: Have the student practice saying each sound/word as he/she goes up the steps. The speech helper will read/say each sound/word. Then, have the student repeat the sounds/words. Practice in front of a mirror when possible.

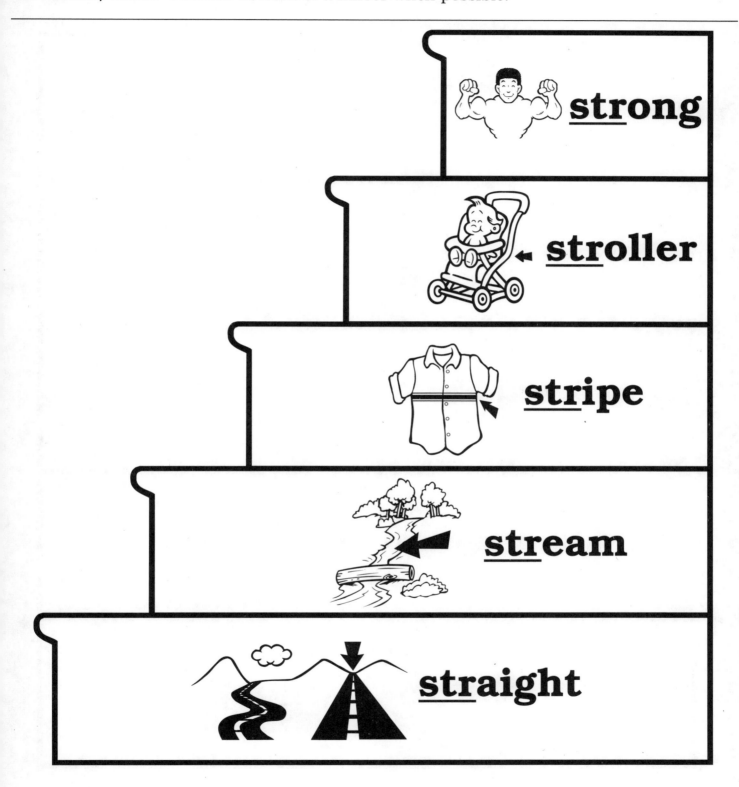

strong

stroller

stripe

stream

straight

Homework Partner   Date   Name

Speech Steps

Instructions: Have the student practice saying each sound/word as he/she goes up the steps. The speech helper will read/say each sound/word. Then, have the student repeat the sounds/words. Practice in front of a mirror when possible.

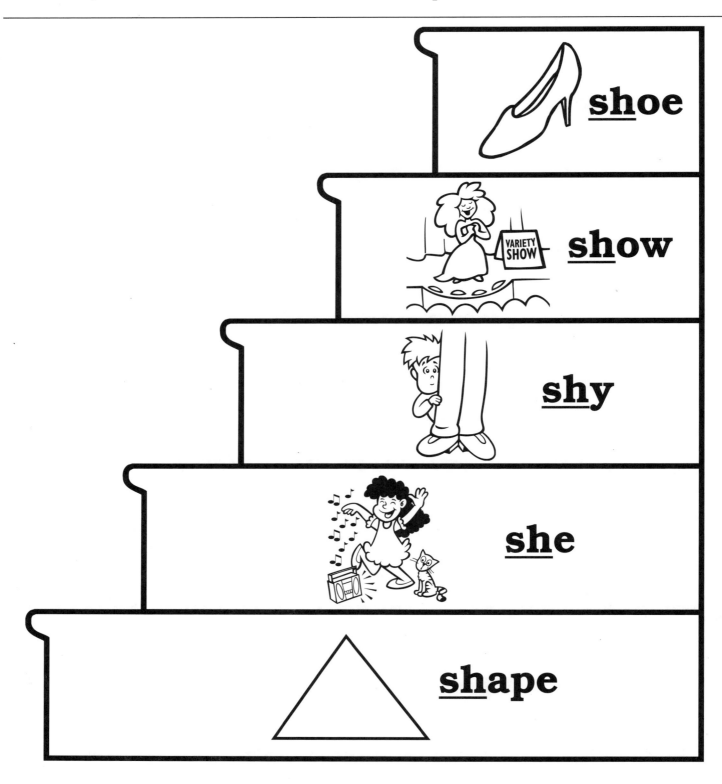

shoe

show

shy

she

shape

Homework Partner   Date   Name

**S Blends
Long Vowels**

#BK-303 Speech Steps® • ©2002 Super Duper® Publications • 1-800-277-8737 • Online! www.superduperinc.com

Speech Steps

Instructions: Have the student practice saying each sound/word as he/she goes up the steps. The speech helper will read/say each sound/word. Then, have the student repeat the sounds/words. Practice in front of a mirror when possible.

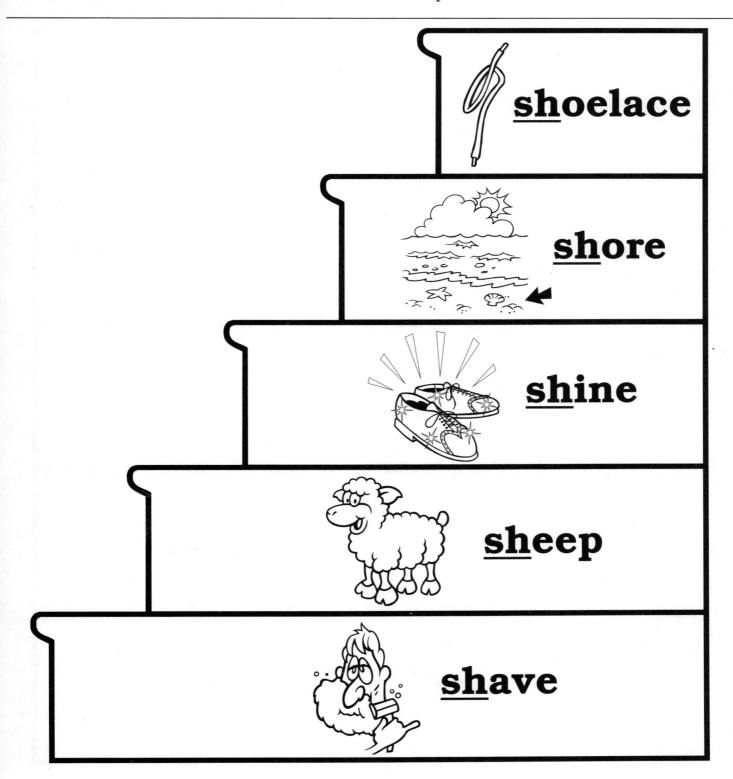

Speech Steps

Instructions: Have the student practice saying each sound/word as he/she goes up the steps. The speech helper will read/say each sound/word. Then, have the student repeat the sounds/words. Practice in front of a mirror when possible.

shut

shop

shin

shell

shack

Speech Steps

Instructions: Have the student practice saying each sound/word as he/she goes up the steps. The speech helper will read/say each sound/word. Then, have the student repeat the sounds/words. Practice in front of a mirror when possible.

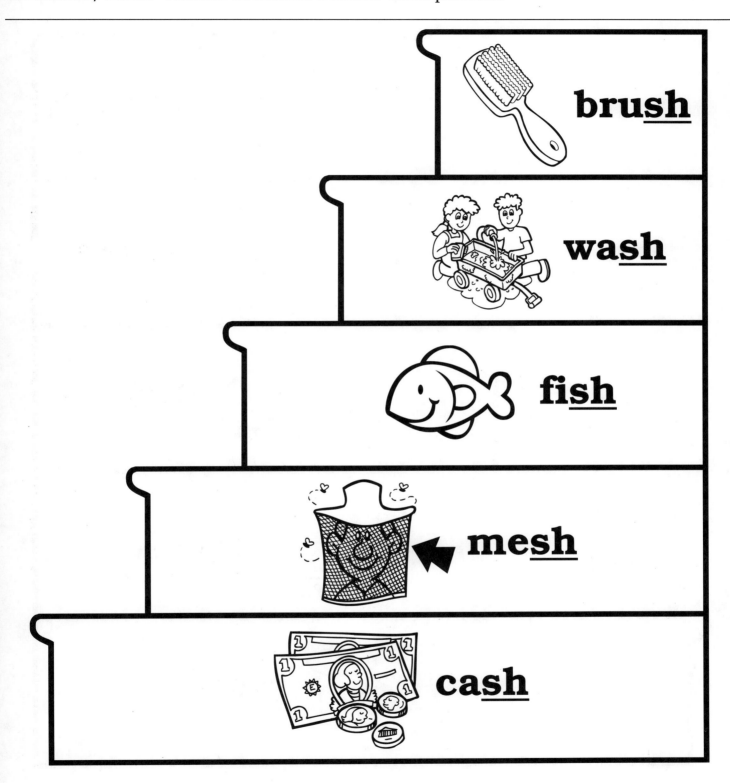

brush

wash

fish

mesh

cash

Homework Partner   Date   Name

Final SH Short Vowels

Speech Steps

Instructions: Have the student practice saying each sound/word as he/she goes up the steps. The speech helper will read/say each sound/word. Then, have the student repeat the sounds/words. Practice in front of a mirror when possible.

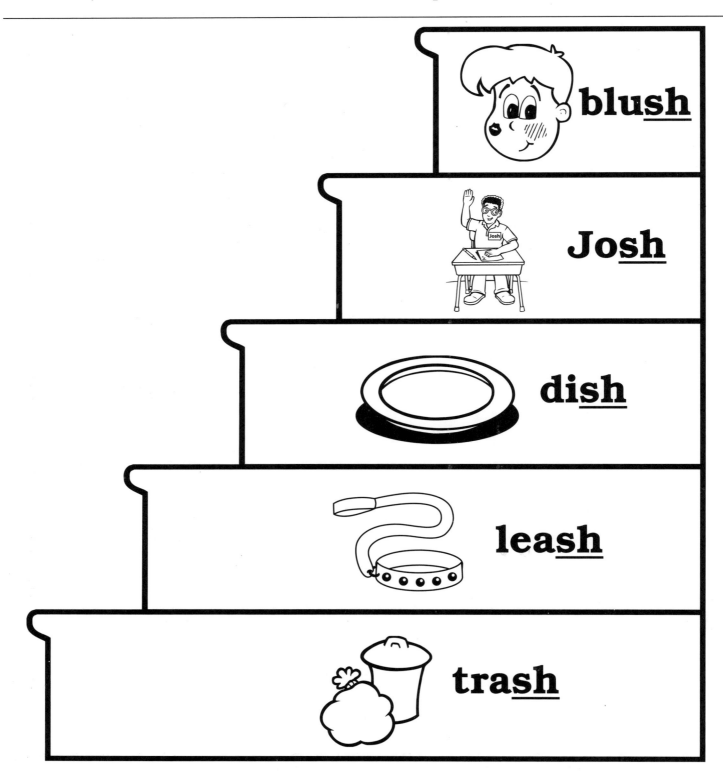

blu**sh**

Jo**sh**

di**sh**

lea**sh**

tra**sh**

Speech Steps

Instructions: Have the student practice saying each sound/word as he/she goes up the steps. The speech helper will read/say each sound/word. Then, have the student repeat the sounds/words. Practice in front of a mirror when possible.

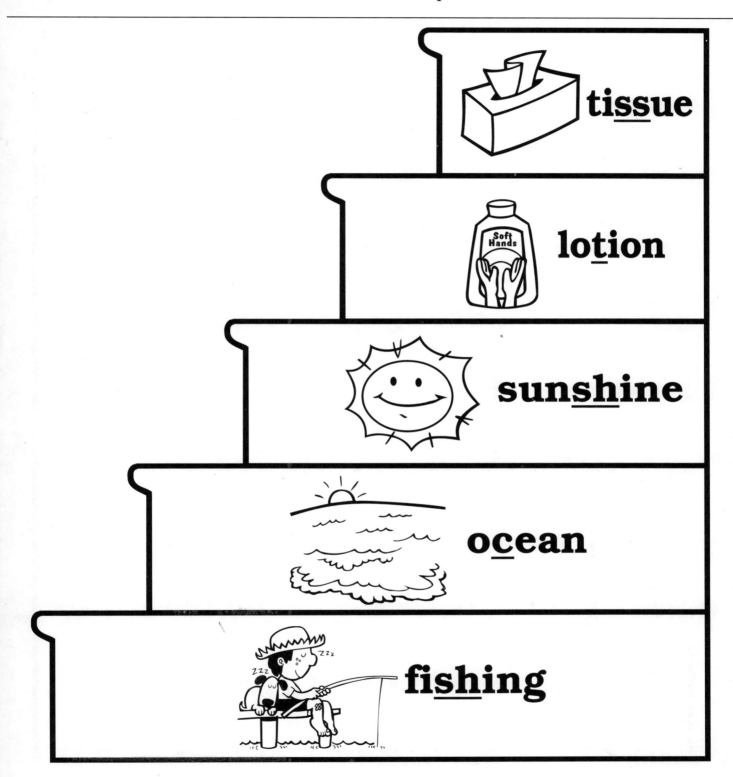

tissue

lotion

sunshine

ocean

fishing

#BK-303 Speech Steps® • ©2002 Super Duper® Publications • 1-800-277-8737 • Online! www.superduperinc.com

Speech Steps

Instructions: Have the student practice saying each sound/word as he/she goes up the steps. The speech helper will read/say each sound/word. Then, have the student repeat the sounds/words. Practice in front of a mirror when possible.

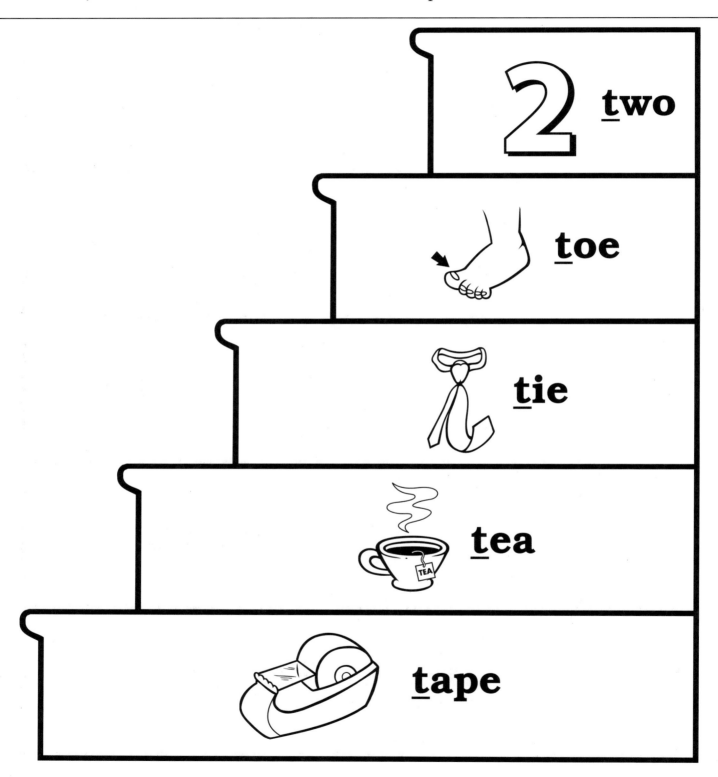

**Initial T
Long Vowels**

#BK-303 Speech Steps® • ©2002 Super Duper® Publications • 1-800-277-8737 • Online! www.superduperinc.com

Speech Steps

Instructions: Have the student practice saying each sound/word as he/she goes up the steps. The speech helper will read/say each sound/word. Then, have the student repeat the sounds/words. Practice in front of a mirror when possible.

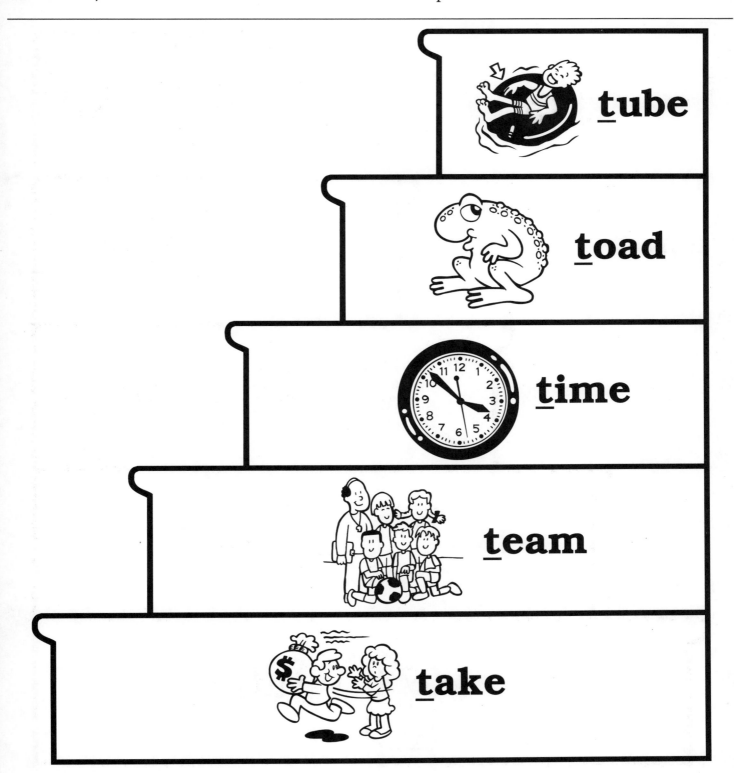

tube

toad

time

team

take

Speech Steps

Instructions: Have the student practice saying each sound/word as he/she goes up the steps. The speech helper will read/say each sound/word. Then, have the student repeat the sounds/words. Practice in front of a mirror when possible.

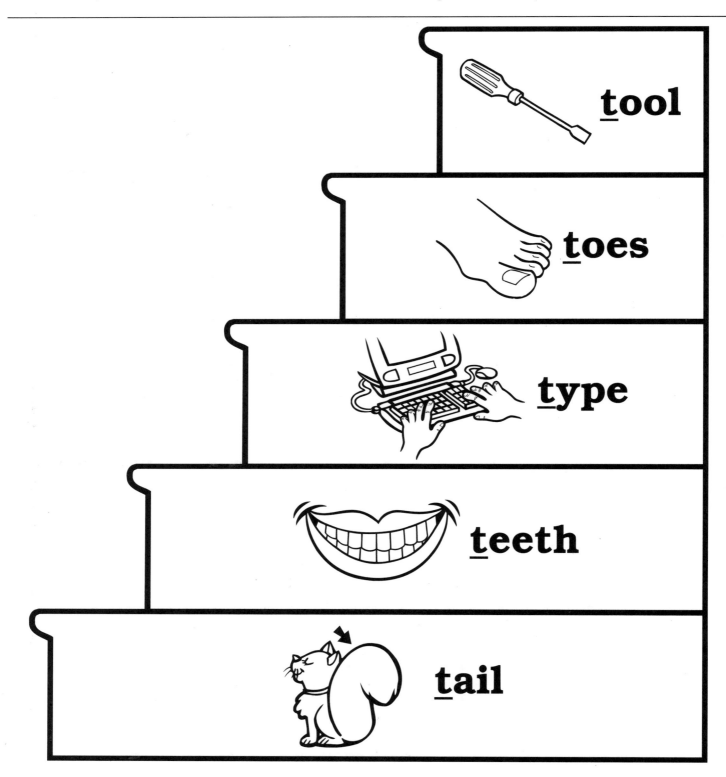

tool

toes

type

teeth

tail

Homework Partner   Date   Name

Initial T Long Vowels

#BK-303 Speech Steps® • ©2002 Super Duper® Publications • 1-800-277-8737 • Online! www.superduperinc.com

Speech Steps

Instructions: Have the student practice saying each sound/word as he/she goes up the steps. The speech helper will read/say each sound/word. Then, have the student repeat the sounds/words. Practice in front of a mirror when possible.

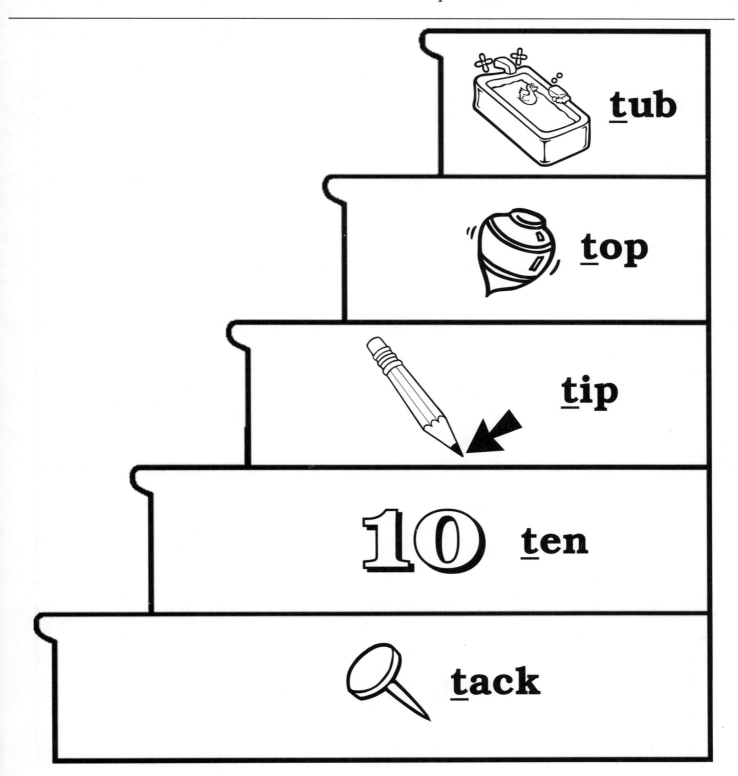

#BK-303 Speech Steps® • ©2002 Super Duper® Publications • 1-800-277-8737 • Online! www.superduperinc.com

Speech Steps

Instructions: Have the student practice saying each sound/word as he/she goes up the steps. The speech helper will read/say each sound/word. Then, have the student repeat the sounds/words. Practice in front of a mirror when possible.

Speech Steps

Instructions: Have the student practice saying each sound/word as he/she goes up the steps. The speech helper will read/say each sound/word. Then, have the student repeat the sounds/words. Practice in front of a mirror when possible.

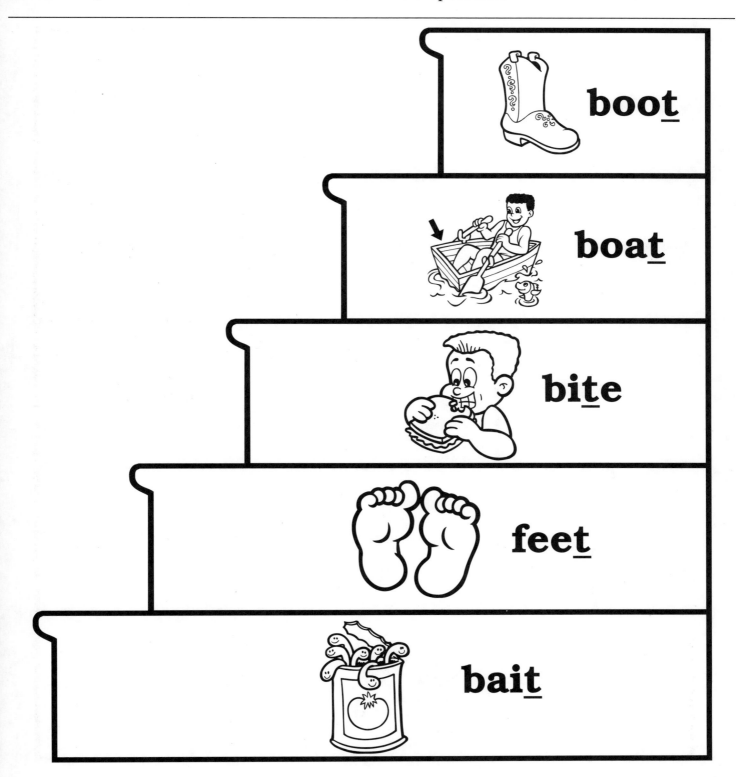

boot

boat

bite

feet

bait

Speech Steps

Instructions: Have the student practice saying each sound/word as he/she goes up the steps. The speech helper will read/say each sound/word. Then, have the student repeat the sounds/words. Practice in front of a mirror when possible.

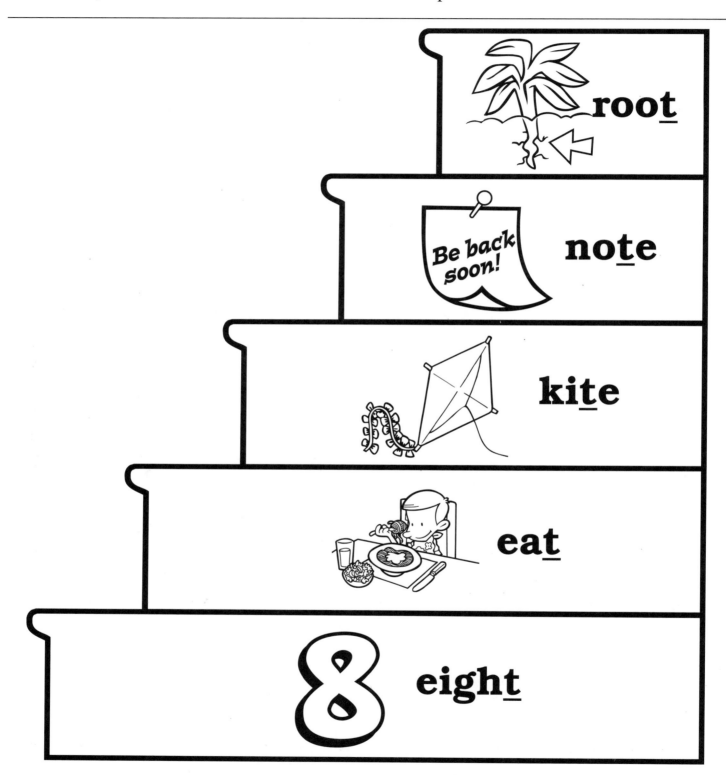

root

note

Be back soon!

kite

eat

8 eight

Final T Long Vowels

Speech Steps

Instructions: Have the student practice saying each sound/word as he/she goes up the steps. The speech helper will read/say each sound/word. Then, have the student repeat the sounds/words. Practice in front of a mirror when possible.

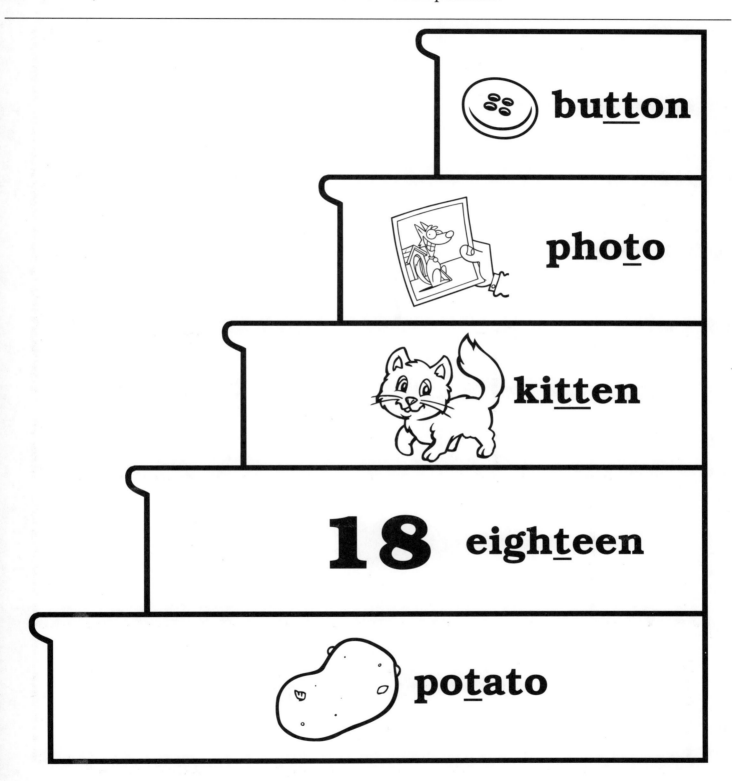

button

photo

kitten

18 eighteen

potato

Speech Steps

Instructions: Have the student practice saying each sound/word as he/she goes up the steps. The speech helper will read/say each sound/word. Then, have the student repeat the sounds/words. Practice in front of a mirror when possible.

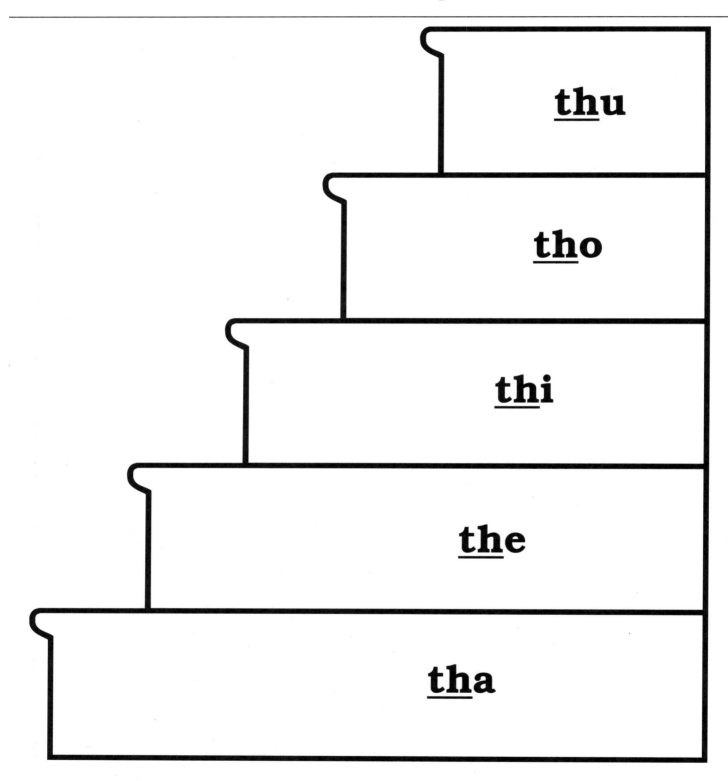

Speech Steps

Instructions: Have the student practice saying each sound/word as he/she goes up the steps. The speech helper will read/say each sound/word. Then, have the student repeat the sounds/words. Practice in front of a mirror when possible.

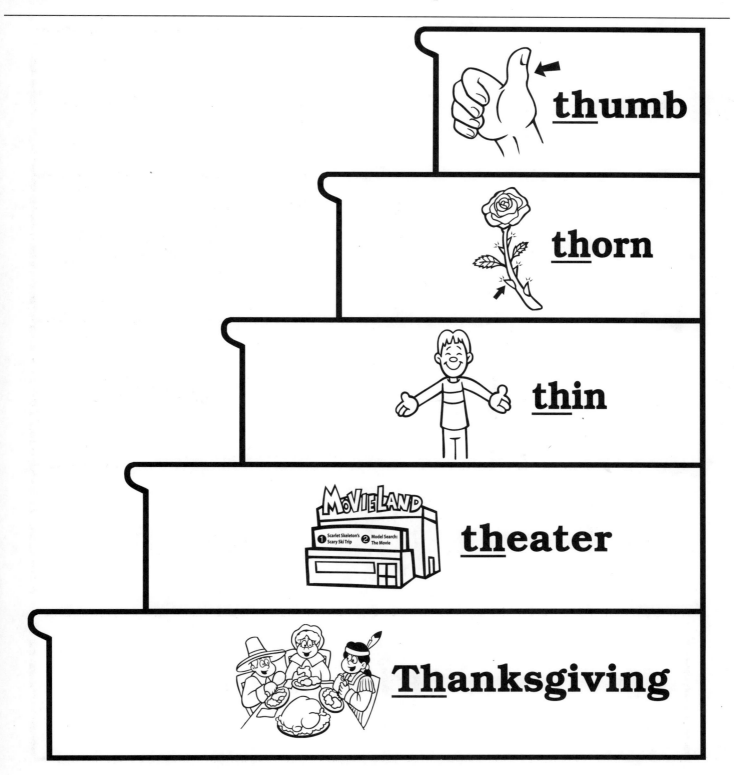

thumb

thorn

thin

theater

Thanksgiving

Homework Partner   Date   Name

Speech Steps

Instructions: Have the student practice saying each sound/word as he/she goes up the steps. The speech helper will read/say each sound/word. Then, have the student repeat the sounds/words. Practice in front of a mirror when possible.

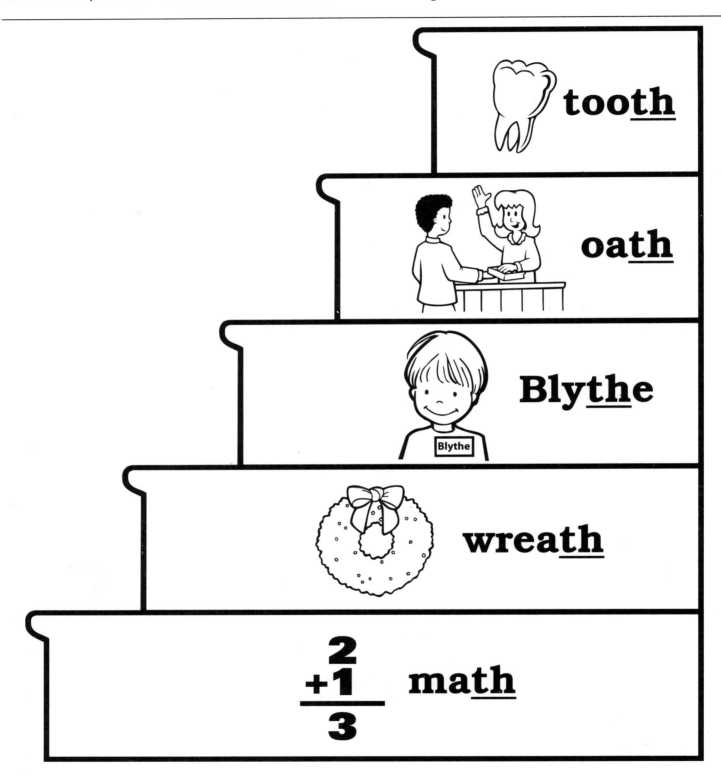

tooth

oath

Blythe

wreath

math

#BK-303 Speech Steps® • ©2002 Super Duper® Publications • 1-800-277-8737 • Online! www.superduperinc.com

Speech Steps

Instructions: Have the student practice saying each sound/word as he/she goes up the steps. The speech helper will read/say each sound/word. Then, have the student repeat the sounds/words. Practice in front of a mirror when possible.

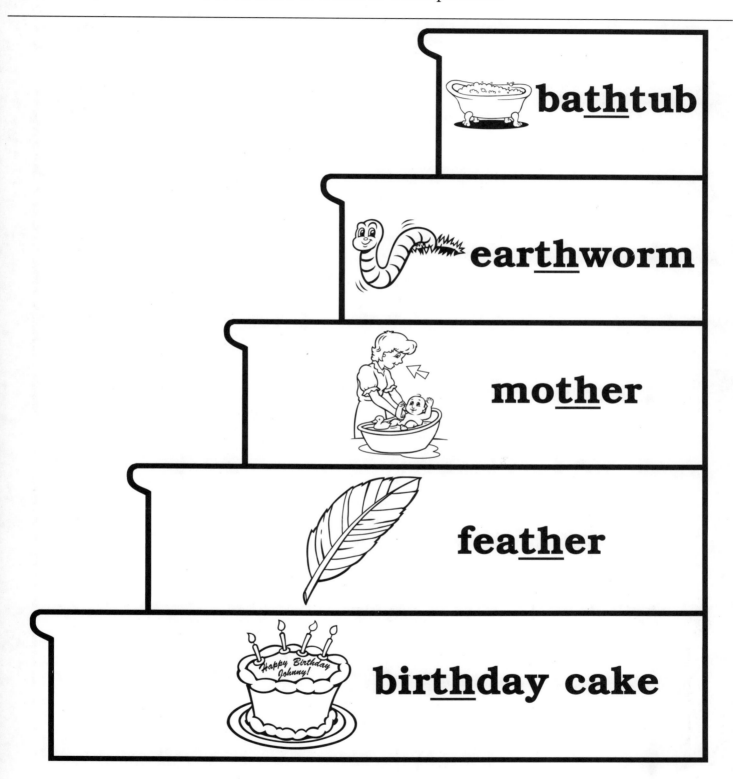

ba**th**tub

ear**th**worm

mo**th**er

fea**th**er

bir**th**day cake

Speech Steps

Instructions: Have the student practice saying each sound/word as he/she goes up the steps. The speech helper will read/say each sound/word. Then, have the student repeat the sounds/words. Practice in front of a mirror when possible.

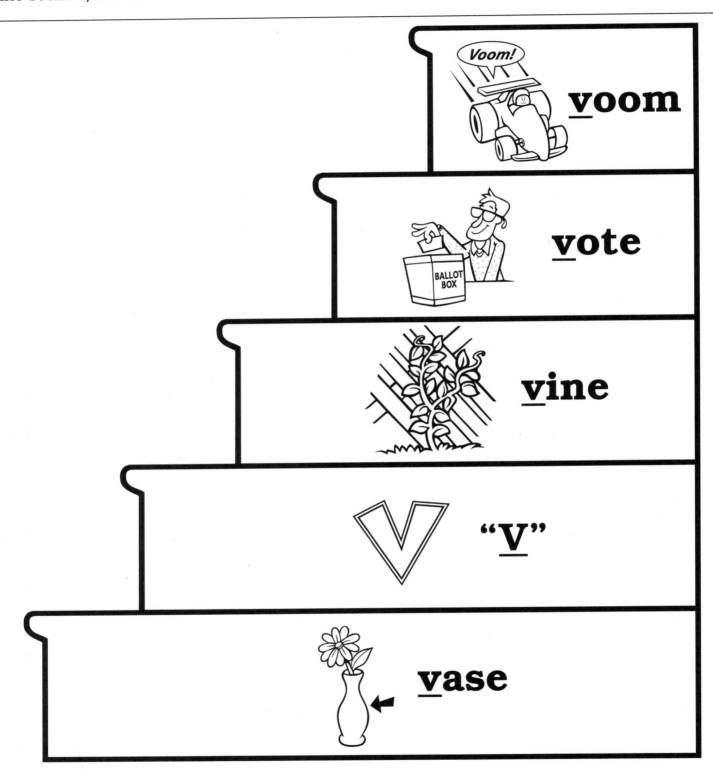

Homework Partner   Date   Name

     #BK-303 Speech Steps® • ©2002 Super Duper® Publications • 1-800-277-8737 • Online! www.superduperinc.com

Speech Steps

Instructions: Have the student practice saying each sound/word as he/she goes up the steps. The speech helper will read/say each sound/word. Then, have the student repeat the sounds/words. Practice in front of a mirror when possible.

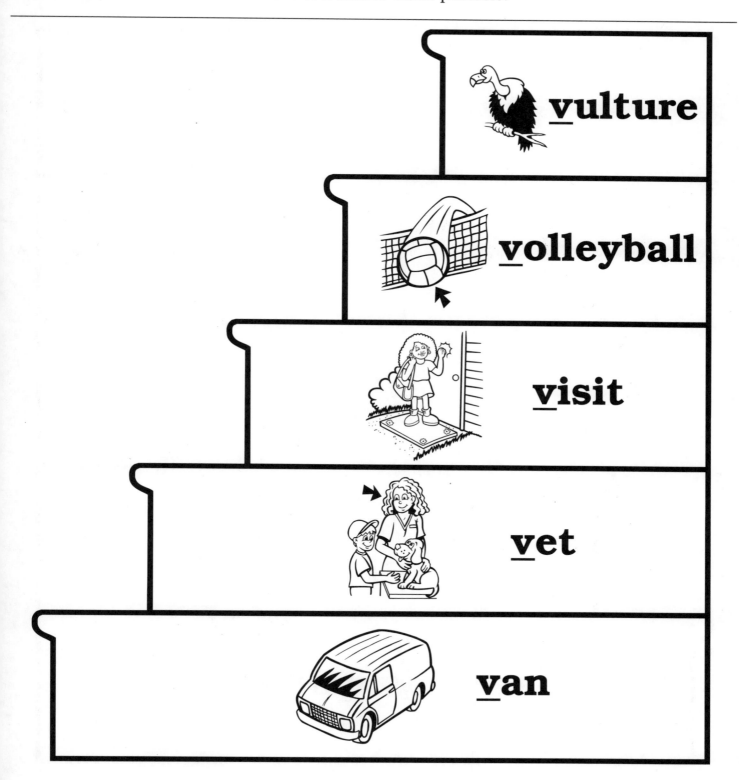

_v_ulture

_v_olleyball

_v_isit

_v_et

_v_an

#BK-303 Speech Steps® • ©2002 Super Duper® Publications • 1-800-277-8737 • Online! www.superduperinc.com

141

Speech Steps

Instructions: Have the student practice saying each sound/word as he/she goes up the steps. The speech helper will read/say each sound/word. Then, have the student repeat the sounds/words. Practice in front of a mirror when possible.

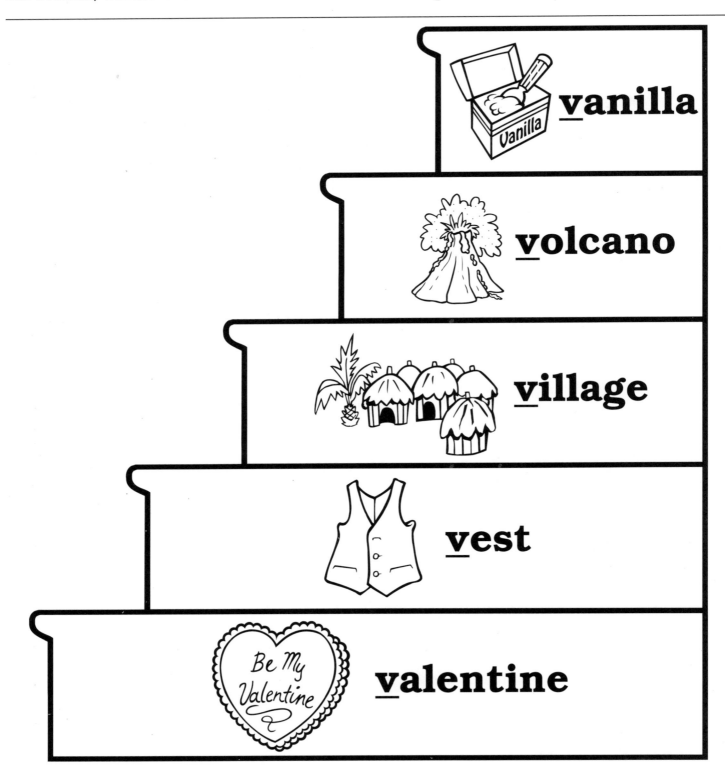

vanilla

volcano

village

vest

valentine

**Initial V
Short Vowels**

#BK-303 Speech Steps® • ©2002 Super Duper® Publications • 1-800-277-8737 • Online! www.superduperinc.com

Speech Steps

Instructions: Have the student practice saying each sound/word as he/she goes up the steps. The speech helper will read/say each sound/word. Then, have the student repeat the sounds/words. Practice in front of a mirror when possible.

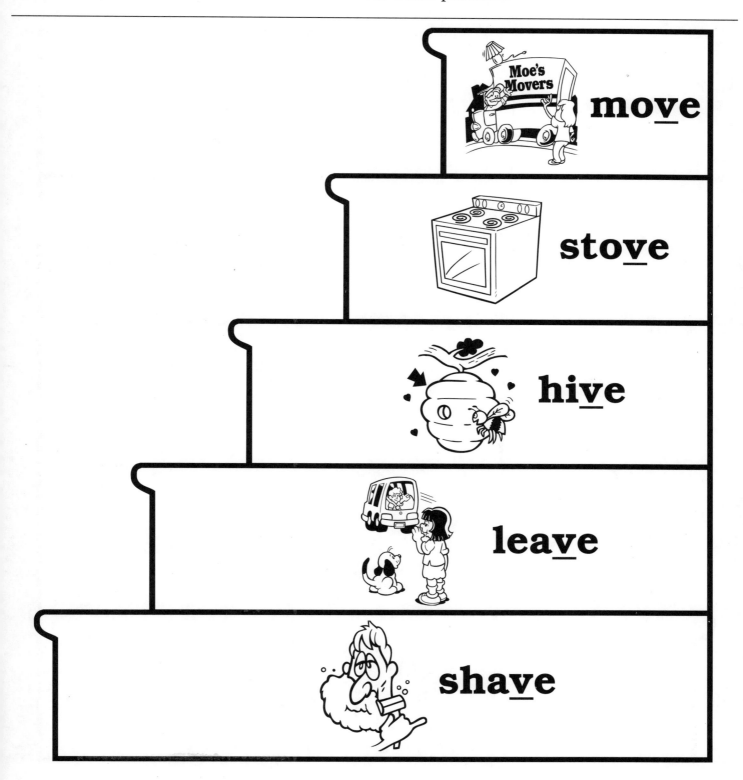

move

stove

hive

leave

shave

Homework Partner   Date   Name

Speech Steps

Instructions: Have the student practice saying each sound/word as he/she goes up the steps. The speech helper will read/say each sound/word. Then, have the student repeat the sounds/words. Practice in front of a mirror when possible.

love

dove

5 five

weave

gave

Speech Steps

Instructions: Have the student practice saying each sound/word as he/she goes up the steps. The speech helper will read/say each sound/word. Then, have the student repeat the sounds/words. Practice in front of a mirror when possible.

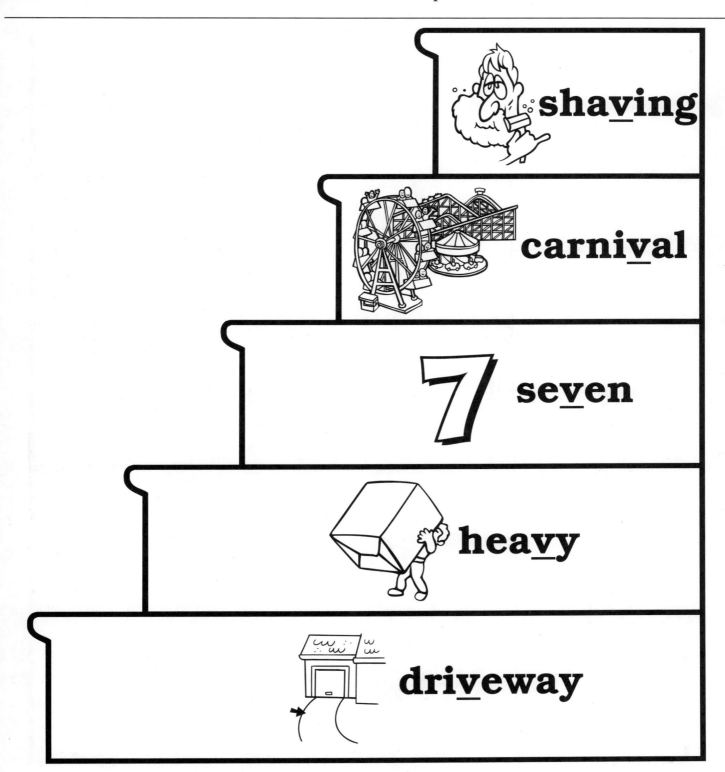

shaving

carnival

7 seven

heavy

driveway

#BK-303 Speech Steps® • ©2002 Super Duper® Publications • 1-800-277-8737 • Online! www.superduperinc.com   145

Speech Steps

Instructions: Have the student practice saying each sound/word as he/she goes up the steps. The speech helper will read/say each sound/word. Then, have the student repeat the sounds/words. Practice in front of a mirror when possible.

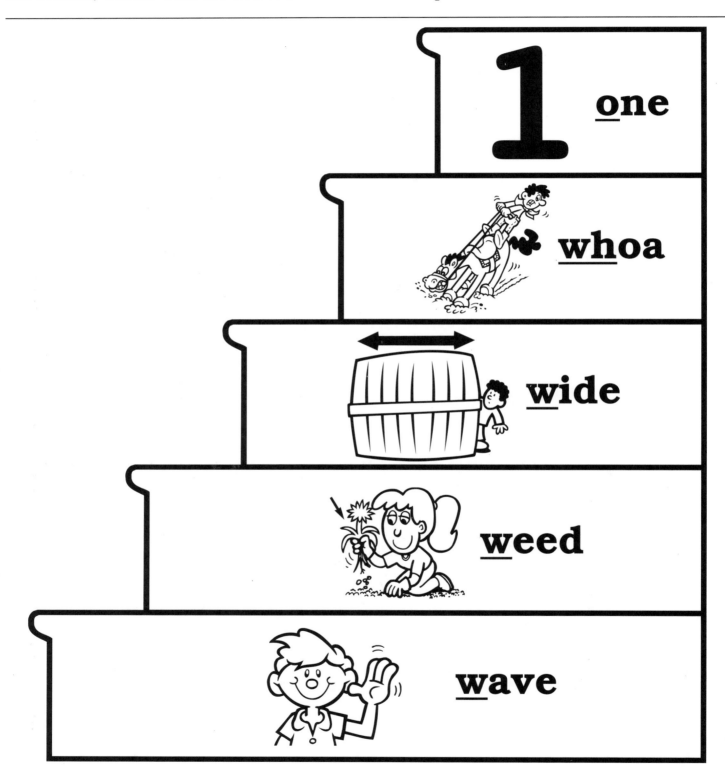

1 <u>o</u>ne

<u>wh</u>oa

<u>w</u>ide

<u>w</u>eed

<u>w</u>ave

Homework Partner   Date   Name

#BK-303 Speech Steps® • ©2002 Super Duper® Publications • 1-800-277-8737 • Online! www.superduperinc.com

Speech Steps

Instructions: Have the student practice saying each sound/word as he/she goes up the steps. The speech helper will read/say each sound/word. Then, have the student repeat the sounds/words. Practice in front of a mirror when possible.

wood

walk

wife

wheel

wait

Speech Steps

Instructions: Have the student practice saying each sound/word as he/she goes up the steps. The speech helper will read/say each sound/word. Then, have the student repeat the sounds/words. Practice in front of a mirror when possible.

woman

watch

wing

we

wade

**Initial W
Combo Vowels**

#BK-303 Speech Steps® • ©2002 Super Duper® Publications • 1-800-277-8737 • Online! www.superduperinc.com

Speech Steps

Instructions: Have the student practice saying each sound/word as he/she goes up the steps. The speech helper will read/say each sound/word. Then, have the student repeat the sounds/words. Practice in front of a mirror when possible.

<u>w</u>ok

<u>w</u>ater

<u>w</u>in

<u>w</u>et

<u>w</u>ag

Homework Partner   Date   Name

Initial W Short Vowels

Speech Steps

Instructions: Have the student practice saying each sound/word as he/she goes up the steps. The speech helper will read/say each sound/word. Then, have the student repeat the sounds/words. Practice in front of a mirror when possible.

Homework Partner	Date	Name	

**Initial B
Short Vowels**

Speech Steps

Instructions: Have the student practice saying each sound/word as he/she goes up the steps. The speech helper will read/say each sound/word. Then, have the student repeat the sounds/words. Practice in front of a mirror when possible.

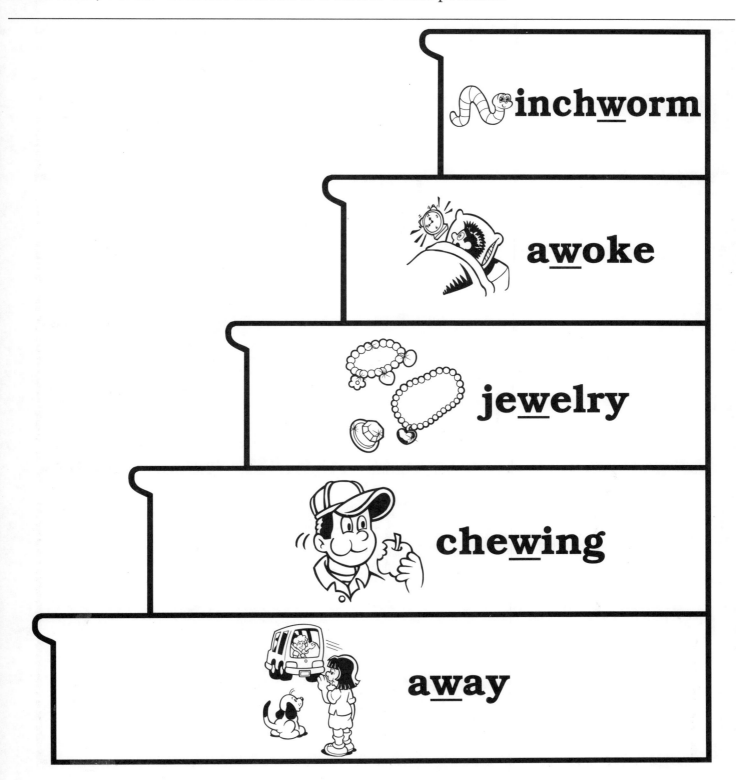

inch**w**orm

a**w**oke

je**w**elry

che**w**ing

a**w**ay

Homework Partner   Date   Name

Medial W Combo Vowels

#BK-303 Speech Steps® • ©2002 Super Duper® Publications • 1-800-277-8737 • Online! www.superduperinc.com   151

Speech Steps

Instructions: Have the student practice saying each sound/word as he/she goes up the steps. The speech helper will read/say each sound/word. Then, have the student repeat the sounds/words. Practice in front of a mirror when possible.

Homework Partner   Date   Name

#BK-303 Speech Steps® • ©2002 Super Duper® Publications • 1-800-277-8737 • Online! www.superduperinc.com

Speech Steps

Instructions: Have the student practice saying each sound/word as he/she goes up the steps. The speech helper will read/say each sound/word. Then, have the student repeat the sounds/words. Practice in front of a mirror when possible.

Homework Partner   Date   Name

Speech Steps

Instructions: Have the student practice saying each sound/word as he/she goes up the steps. The speech helper will read/say each sound/word. Then, have the student repeat the sounds/words. Practice in front of a mirror when possible.

yummy

yogurt

yippee

yes

yam

Homework Partner

Date

Name

#BK-303 Speech Steps® • ©2002 Super Duper® Publications • 1-800-277-8737 • Online! www.superduperinc.com

Speech Steps

Instructions: Have the student practice saying each sound/word as he/she goes up the steps. The speech helper will read/say each sound/word. Then, have the student repeat the sounds/words. Practice in front of a mirror when possible.

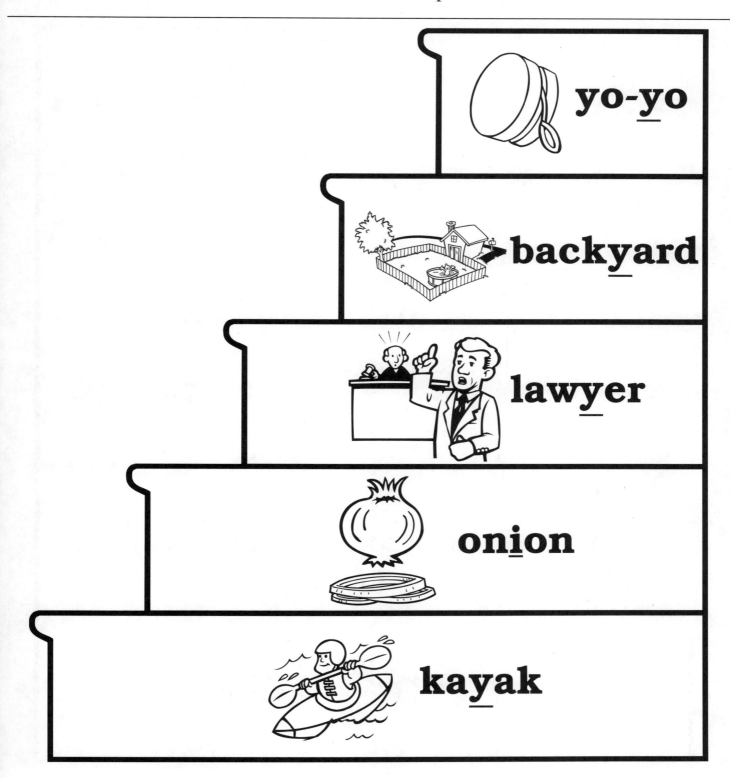

yo-yo

backyard

lawyer

onion

kayak

#BK-303 Speech Steps® • ©2002 Super Duper® Publications • 1-800-277-8737 • Online! www.superduperinc.com

Speech Steps

Instructions: Have the student practice saying each sound/word as he/she goes up the steps. The speech helper will read/say each sound/word. Then, have the student repeat the sounds/words. Practice in front of a mirror when possible.

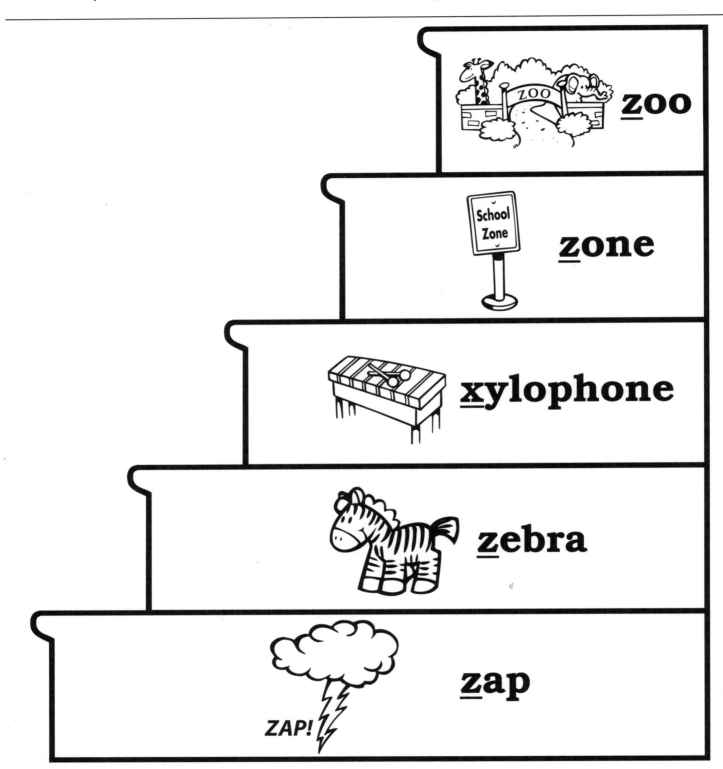

Speech Steps

Instructions: Have the student practice saying each sound/word as he/she goes up the steps. The speech helper will read/say each sound/word. Then, have the student repeat the sounds/words. Practice in front of a mirror when possible.

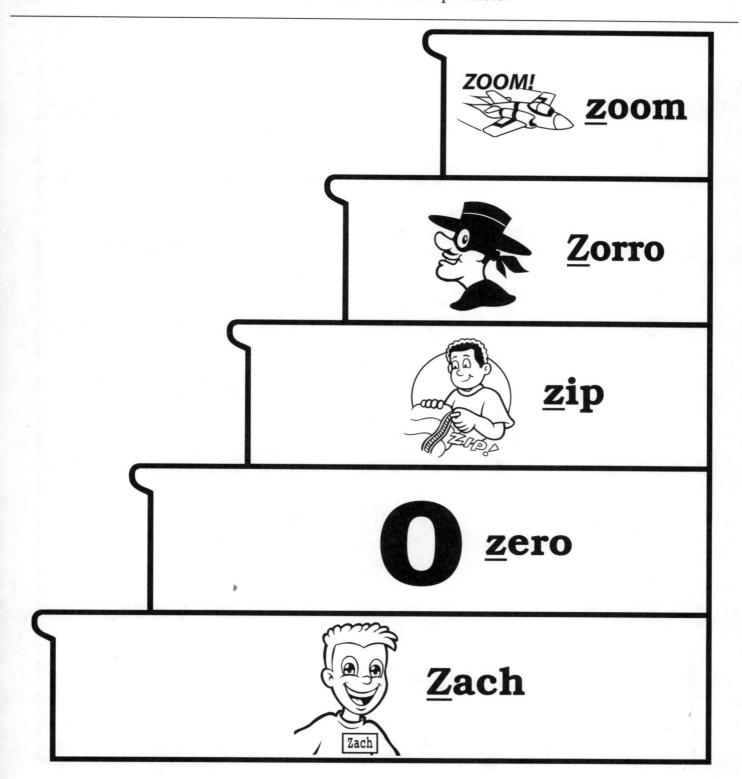

Homework Partner   Date   Name

Initial Z Combo Vowels

#BK-303 Speech Steps® • ©2002 Super Duper® Publications • 1-800-277-8737 • Online! www.superduperinc.com   157

Speech Steps

Instructions: Have the student practice saying each sound/word as he/she goes up the steps. The speech helper will read/say each sound/word. Then, have the student repeat the sounds/words. Practice in front of a mirror when possible.

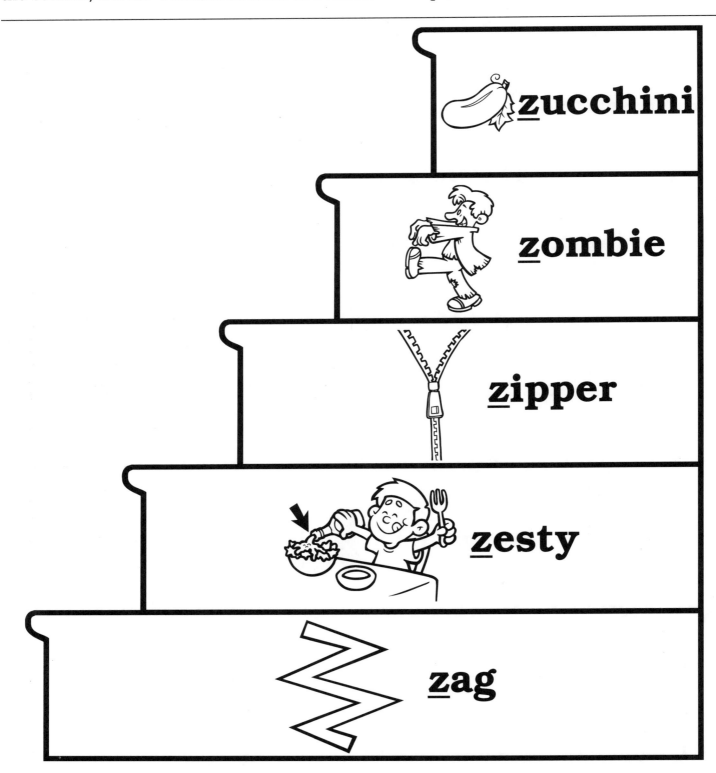

Initial Z Combo Vowels

Speech Steps

Instructions: Have the student practice saying each sound/word as he/she goes up the steps. The speech helper will read/say each sound/word. Then, have the student repeat the sounds/words. Practice in front of a mirror when possible.

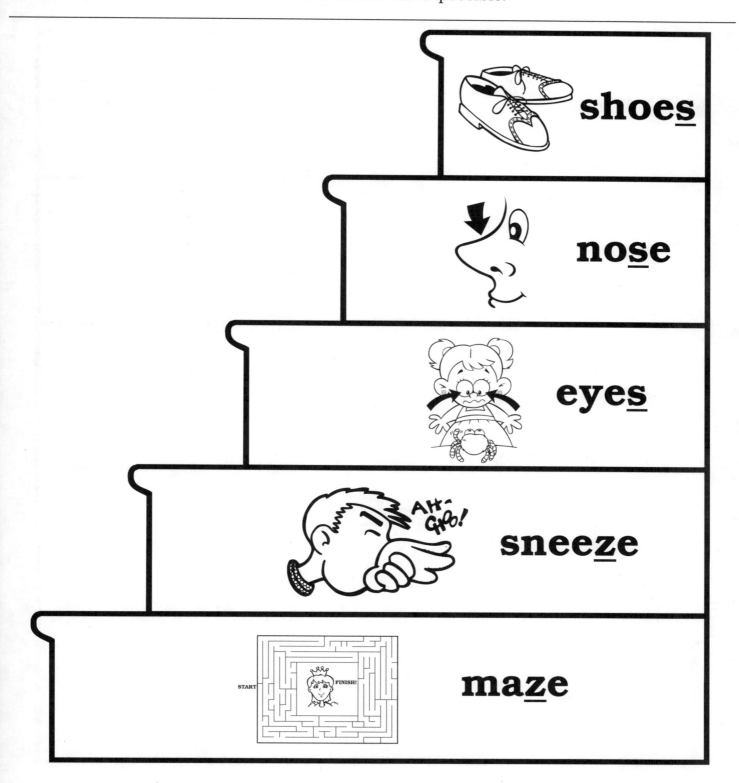

shoe<u>s</u>

no<u>s</u>e

eye<u>s</u>

snee<u>z</u>e

ma<u>z</u>e

Homework Partner   Date   Name

Final Z Long Vowels

Speech Steps

Instructions: Have the student practice saying each sound/word as he/she goes up the steps. The speech helper will read/say each sound/word. Then, have the student repeat the sounds/words. Practice in front of a mirror when possible.

bruise

rose

guys

cheese

raise

Speech Steps

Instructions: Have the student practice saying each sound/word as he/she goes up the steps. The speech helper will read/say each sound/word. Then, have the student repeat the sounds/words. Practice in front of a mirror when possible.

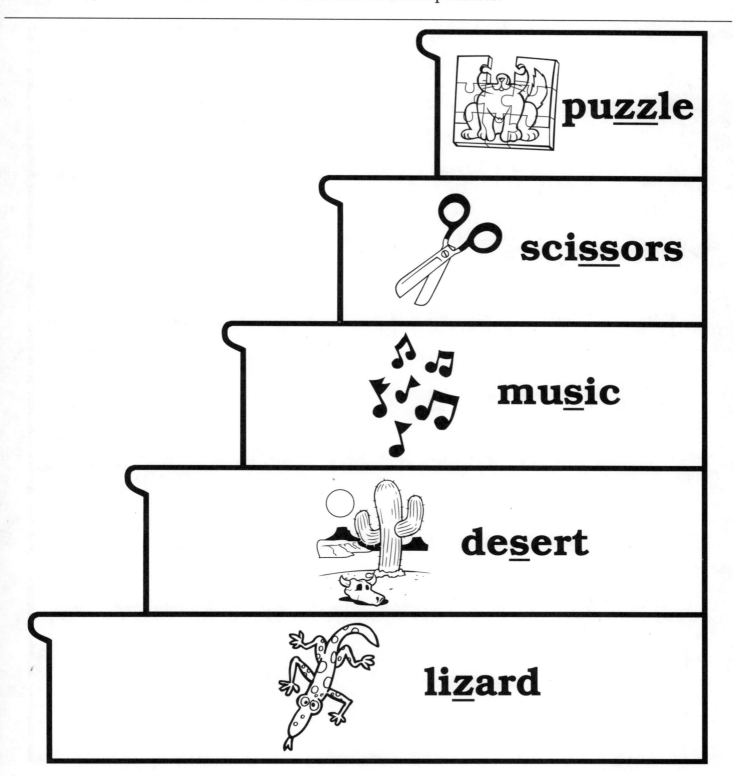

puzzle

scissors

music

desert

lizard

Homework Partner   Date   Name

Medial Z Combo Vowels

#BK-303 Speech Steps® • ©2002 Super Duper® Publications • 1-800-277-8737 • Online! www.superduperinc.com

Speech Steps

Instructions: Have the student practice saying each sound/word as he/she goes up the steps. The speech helper will read/say each sound/word. Then, have the student repeat the sounds/words. Practice in front of a mirror when possible.

Speech Steps

Instructions: Have the student practice saying each sound/word as he/she goes up the steps. The speech helper will read/say each sound/word. Then, have the student repeat the sounds/words. Practice in front of a mirror when possible.

Homework Partner   Date   Name

Speech Steps

Instructions: Have the student practice saying each sound/word as he/she goes up the steps. The speech helper will read/say each sound/word. Then, have the student repeat the sounds/words. Practice in front of a mirror when possible.

Homework Partner   Date   Name

#BK-303 Speech Steps® • ©2002 Super Duper® Publications • 1-800-277-8737 • Online! www.superduperinc.com

Speech Steps

Instructions: Have the student practice saying each sound/word as he/she goes up the steps. The speech helper will read/say each sound/word. Then, have the student repeat the sounds/words. Practice in front of a mirror when possible.

Homework Partner   Date   Name

Speech Steps

Instructions: Have the student practice saying each sound/word as he/she goes up the steps. The speech helper will read/say each sound/word. Then, have the student repeat the sounds/words. Practice in front of a mirror when possible.

Speech Steps

Instructions: Have the student practice saying each sound/word as he/she goes up the steps. The speech helper will read/say each sound/word. Then, have the student repeat the sounds/words. Practice in front of a mirror when possible.

Homework Partner _____ Date _____ Name _____

Speech Steps

Instructions: Have the student practice saying each sound/word as he/she goes up the steps. The speech helper will read/say each sound/word. Then, have the student repeat the sounds/words. Practice in front of a mirror when possible.

Open-Ended Seasonal

Speech Steps

Instructions: Have the student practice saying each sound/word as he/she goes up the steps. The speech helper will read/say each sound/word. Then, have the student repeat the sounds/words. Practice in front of a mirror when possible.

Homework Partner   Date   Name

Open-Ended Seasonal

Speech Steps

Instructions: Have the student practice saying each sound/word as he/she goes up the steps. The speech helper will read/say each sound/word. Then, have the student repeat the sounds/words. Practice in front of a mirror when possible.

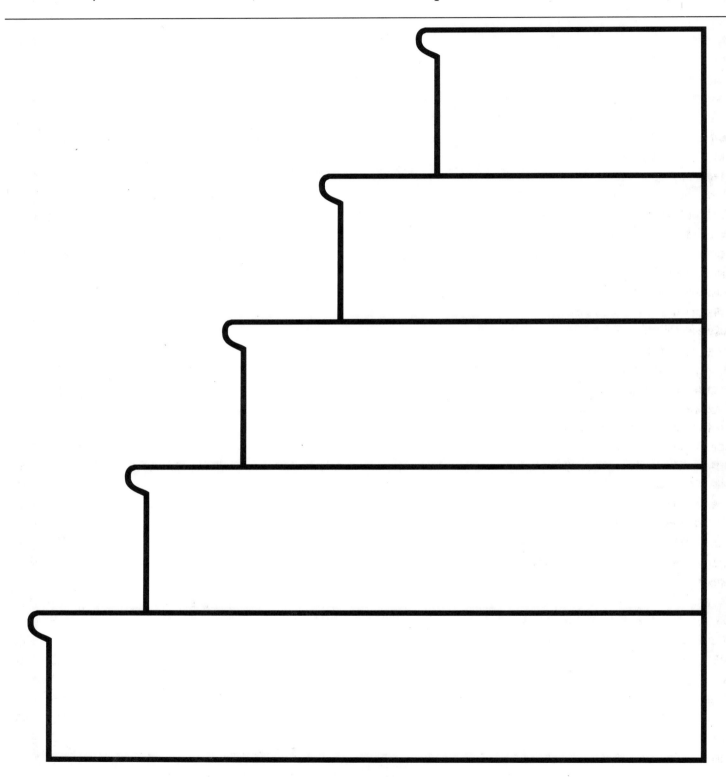

Homework Partner   Date   Name

Blank Open-Ended

#BK-303 Speech Steps® • ©2002 Super Duper® Publications • 1-800-277-8737 • Online! www.superduperinc.com